DR PETER SAUNDERS

THE HUMAN JOURNEY

JOURNEY

THINKING BIBLICALLY ABOUT HEALTH

The Human Journey: Thinking biblically about health
© 2014 Dr Peter Saunders
Dr Peter Saunders has asserted his right under the Copyright, Design and Patents
Act, 1988, to be identified as Author of this work.

Reprinted 2015

Published by Christian Medical Fellowship
6 Marshalsea Road, London SE1 1HL, UK
www.cmf.org.uk

ISBN 978-0-906747-58-2

Printed by Stanley L Hunt Printers Ltd
Cover design and typesetting by S2 Design & Advertising Ltd

In over thirty years as a Christian doctor and speaker only twice can I recall being asked to talk in any church about health. I hope *The Human Journey* will prompt many more churches to consider in depth this vital topic. If Christians are not in good health overall, the church suffers; if churches are not in good health overall, the whole nation suffers. A resource such as this is long overdue.

> *Dr Trevor Stammers, Programme Director for Bioethics and*
> *Medical Law at St Mary's University, Twickenham*

The Human Journey will take you through the highs and lows of the Christian life from both a medical and biblical point of view. The chapter on mental health is well-balanced with helpful practical applications. I would recommend it for both personal reading and group study.

> *Dr Rob Waller, Consultant Psychiatrist, Director of Mind and Soul*
> *www.mindandsoul.info   @robwaller*

The Human Journey is a must-read for those who are not connected to the health professions and an obvious reference for those who are. I believe it makes a major contribution to the study we call 'Christian Worldview'.

> *Stephen Redman, Minister of The Ark Church, York*

The issues *The Human Journey* raises are of critical importance to the future of our culture in Britain. I wholeheartedly recommend this resource to individual Christians and to the wider church.

> *Rico Tice, All Souls Church & Christianity Explored*

The Human Journey applies the plumb line of Scripture to contemporary health issues. When there are so many new treatments being offered through modern medicine, it is important that Christians are well-informed as they as face decisions about personal health. *The Human Journey* also gives churches and church leaders vital guidelines to think through pastoral issues relating to health and wellbeing, and to engage effectively in debates on the medical ethical issues facing our society.

> *Catherine Butcher, Communications Director, HOPE*

Peter Saunders was born in New Zealand and originally trained as a general surgeon, before serving with the Africa Inland Mission (AIM) at Kapsowar Hospital in Kenya and then completing two years' mission training at All Nations Christian College in the UK.

Since 1992 he has served full-time with Christian Medical Fellowship (CMF), a UK-based organisation with a membership of 4,500 UK doctors and 1,000 medical students, first as Head of Student Ministries and since 1999 as Chief Executive.

His current work involves leadership training, teaching evangelism and ethics, medical mission, writing, editing and media work. He is also Campaign Director of the Care Not Killing Alliance, a coalition of over 40 organisations in the UK promoting palliative care and opposing euthanasia, and chair of the European Euthanasia Prevention Coalition.

Peter has been a member of the International Christian Medical and Dental Association (ICMDA) board since 2003 and also serves on the Coalition for Marriage board and the European Leadership Forum (ELF) steering group.

His wife Kirsty is a community paediatrician and they have three sons Christopher, Benjamin and Jonathan. They are members of Spicer Street Church, St Albans.

3

CONTENTS

ACKNOWLEDGEMENTS

The Human Journey, with its accompanying videos, study guide and website was a project dreamt up by the communications department of the Christian Medical Fellowship, with the aim of helping Christians apply a biblical mindset to issues at the interface of Christianity and healthcare. As the CEO of CMF I was asked to write the book, but received assistance from many others with an interest in seeing the enterprise come to fruition.

My predecessor Andrew Fergusson and I worked together on the basic outline, devising the eight chapter categories and making broad decisions about content. The study guide was written by CMF head of communications John Martin and communications coordinator Tom Roberts. The videos were directed and produced by CMF media producer Andrew Horton and the website and book were designed by Darren Southworth of S2 Design & Advertising.

Members of the CMF staff read drafts of the book and contributed to many improvements: Alex Bunn, Catherine Butcher, Giles Cattermole, Laurence Crutchlow, Pablo Fernandez, Steve Fouch, Vicky Lavy, Philippa Taylor and Rick Thomas. Other CMF members and friends read later drafts and helped to improve it further: Helen Barratt, Chris Damant, Andrew Fergusson, Mark Houghton, Peter May, Huw Morgan, Mark Pickering, Stephen Redman, Maggy Spence, Trevor Stammers, Rob Waller and Derrett Watts.

The aforementioned members of the CMF communications department saw the project through and I'm particularly grateful to Andrew Horton who offered valued input and constant encouragement, Tom Roberts who did the copy editing and John Martin who oversaw the whole enterprise.

Finally, I'd like to thank my wife Kirsty and three sons Chris, Ben and Jonno, for their inspiration and support in seeing it completed. The book has truly been a team effort, but despite this, any errors, omissions, inaccuracies and doctrinal emphases are my responsibility and mine alone.

M any people today hold an atheist worldview – God doesn't exist, human beings are just clever monkeys, morality is largely a matter of personal choice and death is the end. Within this framework medical technology can become simply a tool to improve life's length and quality without regard to any overall meaning and purpose. If we want it and can do it and it seems to improve our life and health then why not?

By contrast, the Bible teaches that God does indeed exist, and that he has clearly spoken and acted in history in a way that leaves us in no doubt about his character and intentions. He has created human beings to know him and love him. Death is not the end at all but rather a gateway to two radically different futures – either to enjoy eternity with God in a new and perfect world, or to be excluded from his presence forever. Under this scheme, history is indeed 'his story' – a divine drama worked out according to God's will and purpose. Consequently how we use medical technology and think about our health in God's world matters immensely.

The Human Journey aims to equip Christians to think biblically about health. But the issues covered need to be seen in the greater context of God's design for man, the universe and everything – his great plan of redemption to unite everything under Jesus Christ. We will begin by sketching out the grand 'metanarrative' – the overarching storyline of the Bible in which all our individual stories make sense. Don't be tempted to skip this. It makes sense of all that follows. Having laid this foundation we will then focus in on issues at the interface of Christianity and health under eight big themes – each accompanied by a key question:

- **Humanity**: What does it mean to be human?
- **Start of Life**: When does life begin?
- **Marriage & Sexuality**: What is marriage for?
- **Physical Health**: How should I live?
- **Mental Health**: Am I supposed to feel like this?
- **End of Life**: How should life end?
- **New Technologies**: Are we playing God?
- **Global Health**: Who is my neighbour?

The Human Journey has two main aims:

1. To establish a biblical framework that will help Christians and churches engage wisely and sensitively with current issues relating to health.
2. To encourage more effective incorporation of healthcare expertise into pastoral life and ministry.

While the book can be read alone, it is accompanied by a set of videos and a study guide for small groups, expanding on each chapter. It's intended to be shared and discussed within the context of *The Human Journey* course. The personal stories interspersed throughout are fictional but based on real events and are included to help bring the biblical principles to life. To help you explore the issues we touch upon in more depth, there are also a host of articles and further resources at *www.humanjourney.org.uk*

My desire is to see people excited about the whole Bible, more amazed about Christ's great work and all that it means and more confident about how to bring God's word and healthcare together. So I have deliberately packed this book full of biblical references. If you finish it more grateful for all God has done and is doing, hungrier to mine the depths of Scripture and better equipped to think, serve and speak for Jesus Christ then it will have achieved its aim.

Dr Peter Saunders

THE DIVINE DRAMA

W e are all on the Human Journey – from birth to death, through health and sickness. We are all part of life's adventure. But our limited human perspectives can only be understood in the light of God's perfect perspective. Each and every human journey is played out on the stage of a grand divine drama that encompasses all of history. This drama was planned and set in motion before the universe began. But God has not left us like actors stumbling in the dark without a script. Thankfully he has provided us with all we need to know about his great plan, his *divine drama*, in the Bible.

If we are to think biblically about health, then we first need to think biblically. We cannot gain a Christian perspective on medicine and health without first seeing how they fit into God's great plan of salvation. So it's essential at the outset that we don't dive in before taking time to understand what the Bible is all about. The Bible provides the framework.

A book like no other

The Bible helps us to understand Christ's mission and the big story of God's intervention in history. The apostle Paul says that the Bible is 'the sword of the Spirit' (Ephesians 6:17). It's literally 'God-breathed' (2 Timothy 3:16).

The word 'Bible' means 'books' – the Bible is actually a collection of 66 different books written by over 30 different authors across three continents in three languages over a period of 1,500 years, which has been carefully compiled from reliable copies of the original manuscripts. It is arranged in two main sections. The Old Testament, containing 39 books, starts with the creation narrative and ends with the Jewish people returning to the land of Israel from exile in the sixth century BC. The New Testament, with 27 books, begins about 400 years later with the birth of Jesus Christ. It ends with the establishment of the Christian church in the first century AD, and gives a glorious view of the future when Christ returns.

The Old Testament consists of history, prophecy and wisdom literature (poems, songs and proverbs). The New Testament contains accounts of the life of Christ and his apostles along with letters written by the apostles to early churches and church leaders. The Bible's account of human history is linear with a beginning, middle and end. It begins with two people in a garden and ends in a city with 'a great multitude that no one could count, from every nation, tribe, people and language' (Revelation 7:9).

The biblical metanarrative (or big story) tells of God's great salvation plan through Jesus Christ. We get the first hint of Jesus in Genesis 1 where he is God's Word bringing the universe into being. In the very last verses of Revelation he comes to collect his bride, the church. The Bible, quite simply, is all about Jesus!

We can summarise the biblical narrative under four main themes: Creation, Fall, Salvation and New Creation. The bulk of the Bible deals with the story of salvation, the account of God's plan to rescue his people, to reveal his kingdom here on earth through his people and to reconcile the universe to himself. Understanding how this story unfolds, and therefore how each book fits into it, is the key to knowing, loving and applying it.

Let's therefore examine the basic historical skeleton of the Old Testament on which all of its individual stories hang and begin to make sense.

Creation, rebellion and promise

The Bible begins with the account of creation (Genesis 1–2), the Fall
(Genesis 3) and the establishment of civilisation (Genesis 4–5). After
God made the universe he created human beings in his own image to
know and love him, but they rebelled against his rule, shattering their
relationships with each other, with creation and with God himself.
This rebellion of the first human beings – known as the Fall – led the
entire human race into rebellion until 'every inclination of the
thoughts of the human heart was only evil all the time' (Genesis 6:5).
Then God sent the Flood, from which only Noah and his family were
saved in the ark (Genesis 6–9). After further massive population
growth and the formation of the nations, people rebelled again and
built the tower of Babel. This led to a further intervention by God
who confused their language, thus creating distinct cultural groups,
and scattered them throughout the earth (Genesis 10–11). But then
God's rescue plan began. It was in Haran – near the border between
Turkey and Syria today – that God called Abram (later to be renamed
Abraham) and made him a wonderful promise:

> Go from your country, your people and your father's
> household to the land I will show you.
> I will make you into a great nation, and I will bless you;
> I will make your name great, and you will be a blessing.
> I will bless those who bless you, and whoever curses you I will curse;
> and all peoples on earth will be blessed through you.
> (Genesis 12:1–3)

There are three main parts to this promise: a land, a nation and a
blessing to all nations. The rest of Genesis (chapters 12–50) tells the
story of the Patriarchs, Abraham's son Isaac and his grandson Jacob,
who would be renamed Israel. God repeats his promise of offspring
to both Isaac and Jacob (Genesis 22:17–18, 26:4, 28:13–14) but
Genesis ends with the family in Egypt where they are to be slaves.
The nation of Israel has been born. Later we will learn that God's
promise of 'offspring' has a double meaning. It refers to the nation of
Israel, but also to Jesus Christ himself (Genesis 3:15; Galatians 3:16–19).

Exodus, kingdom and conquest

The book of Exodus recounts Israel's liberation from slavery in Egypt under the leadership of Moses. Comparing the biblical record to the best available evidence outside the Bible dates this event to about 1446 BC. After Israel's liberation, God makes a covenant with his chosen people, gives them the Ten Commandments and establishes the sacrificial system that is to maintain their on-going relationship with him. Both the moral law and the temple sacrifices foreshadow the coming of Christ.

After their deliverance from Egypt, the nation of Israel rebels against God resulting in a prolonged stay in the Sinai desert. But after 40 years in the wilderness (covered in Leviticus, Numbers and Deuteronomy), God brings this nation of former slaves, under Joshua's leadership, into Canaan – the promised land. The conquest of this land follows, recounted in the book of Joshua. The nation of Israel settles in the land under the leadership of Judges like Gideon and Samson, who rescue them from the attacks of surrounding nations. Eventually leadership of the nation falls to the prophet Samuel. Looking with envy at the nations around them, the people demand a king and Samuel reluctantly establishes the Israelite monarchy, anointing Saul as the first king, who is later succeeded by David (1 and 2 Samuel). During the reign of David's son Solomon, the nation of Israel enjoys its glory days, but following this the story is one of division and general decline.

Division and exile

When Rehoboam, Solomon's son, becomes king, the ten northern tribes of Israel revolt and become a separate nation (1 Kings 12). After years of attrition, and in spite of the warnings of prophets like Elijah and Amos, this northern kingdom is finally destroyed by the Assyrians in 721 BC and its inhabitants are lost to the pages of history (2 Kings 17).

The southern kingdom, renamed Judah (from which the word 'Jew' is derived) is finally overthrown by the Babylonians in 587 BC and its people taken into exile (2 Kings 25; 2 Chronicles 36). During this period, through Daniel and his friends, the nation's faith is rekindled, and they understand from the words of the prophet Jeremiah (Jeremiah 25:8–14) that they will return to their promised land.

Seventy years after being exiled to Babylon they return with the blessing of King Cyrus of Persia, the new global power, and re-establish the nation of Israel under the leadership of Zerubbabel, Ezra and Nehemiah. The prophets Malachi, Zechariah and Haggai provide encouragement and guidance during this period.

Throughout all these centuries, in spite of God's on-going faithfulness, the people of Israel repeatedly reject him, break his covenant and fail to become the blessing to other nations outlined in God's promise to Abraham. The military defeats and later destruction of Israel are a consequence of this rejection.

The coming king

Through the Prophets, who repeatedly call Israel back into a faithful relationship with God, he promises to establish a New Covenant with them, in which he will write his law on their hearts (Jeremiah 31:31–34), cleanse them, regenerate them and enable them to live in obedience to him (Ezekiel 36:24–26). These promises ultimately find their fulfilment in the coming of Jesus Christ.

There is a gap of just over 400 years between the ministry of the final Old Testament prophet Malachi and the birth of Jesus. This is called the 'inter-testamental period' as it is not covered by either Old or New Testaments. During this period the Greeks, under the leadership of Alexander the Great, take over from the Persians as the predominant world power. When Alexander dies, his empire is divided into four parts, as prophesied by Daniel, and the Jews undergo a further period of terrible persecution under the Greek General Antiochus IV. Under the leadership of the Maccabees they throw off the oppressive Greek yoke. Events of this period are recorded in the books of the Apocrypha which are not regarded as being inspired by God and so are not included in most Bibles. The Greek Empire is then overturned by the Romans, who invade Jerusalem in 63 BC. When Jesus is born some 60 years later, Israel is still under Roman occupation.

As the Old Testament progresses it becomes clear that the real children of Abraham are not just those who are biologically descended from him but rather those who share his faith in God. They are to come from all nations. The instrument by which God's salvation will come to all the nations is not the nation of Israel itself but rather one man, the *Messiah*.

The *Messiah*, meaning 'Anointed One', is identified in the Old Testament by a variety of titles and roles. He is called the Son of God (Psalm 2) and the Son of Man to whom the nations of the world will be given as an inheritance (Daniel 7:13–14). The prophet Isaiah calls him the Servant and tells us that he will suffer and die on behalf of his people (Isaiah 53). Moses calls him the Prophet who will bring God's message (Deuteronomy 18:14–22) and the Psalms refer to him as the Bridegroom who will form a deep intimate relationship with his people and will reign forever (Psalm 45). In other places he is called the Prince of Peace (Isaiah 9:6–7) and the Chosen One (Psalm 89).

The Bible tells us that this one man will be descended through Abraham, Isaac and Jacob, Judah, Jesse, David and Zerubbabel. The Gospels of Matthew and Luke complete this genealogy for us, showing the person to be none other than Jesus Christ (Matthew 1:1–17; Luke 3:23–37).

The Lamb of God

The New Testament's message is that Jesus is the Messiah (John 1:41) and that in him Jews and Gentiles (non-Jews) can be reconciled to God and united as one. Many of the Old Testament passages above make it clear that this Messiah is not only a man, with flesh and blood, but is also God himself (eg Isaiah 9:6), Matthew claims the title of 'Immanuel' for him – God with us (Matthew 1:22–23). John the Baptist identifies Jesus as the Lamb of God, who takes away the sin of the world (John 1:29). The significance of this title is drawn from the Old Testament. During the first Passover in Egypt the spreading of a lamb's blood over the doorways of the Israelite homes protected the eldest sons from the destroying angel, the instrument of God's judgment. The Egyptians, without such protection, died (Exodus 11– 12). The elaborate Jewish sacrificial system (Leviticus 1–9), which involved the slaughter of thousands of animals for the sins of the Israelites, protected God's people from the wrath and judgment that they rightly deserved. The Day of Atonement, the holiest day of the Jewish calendar, involved sending a goat, on which the sins of Israel had been placed, out into the wilderness (Leviticus 16).

In all of these instances a temporary reprieve was achieved for sinful human beings. But the real purpose of these sacrifices was to foreshadow and point forward to the death of Jesus, the Lamb of God, on the cross, which would deal with sin once and for all. So Jesus is called the 'Lamb of God' because like the Passover lamb his death was an act of *substitutionary atonement*. In other words Jesus died *in our place*, receiving the punishment that our sins deserved. This teaching is at the very heart of the Christian faith; God makes peace with estranged, guilty and rebellious human beings through the death of his Son Jesus Christ. As sinful human beings we all fall short of God's standards and deserve God's condemnation. Because Jesus has taken that wrath and judgment in our place, we receive God's grace and mercy and are thereby forgiven. Our sins had to be paid for. But because we could not pay for them ourselves, Jesus did so on our behalf.

Isaiah 53, the last of the four 'servant songs', written 700 years before Christ was crucified, predicts his death and its meaning in astonishing detail:

> *Surely he took up our pain and bore our suffering,*
> *yet we considered him punished by God,*
> *stricken by him, and afflicted.*
> *But he was pierced for our transgressions,*
> *he was crushed for our iniquities;*

the punishment that brought us peace was on him,
and by his wounds we are healed.
We all, like sheep, have gone astray,
each of us has turned to our own way;
and the Lord has laid on him the iniquity of us all.
(Isaiah 53:4–6)

In the same way, substitutionary atonement is equally the central teaching of the New Testament. Paul says that Jesus died 'for us' (Romans 5:8; 1 Thessalonians 5:10) and also that he died 'for our sins' (1 Corinthians 15:3; Galatians 1:4). Jesus describes his own ministry as giving his life 'as a ransom for many' (Mark 10:45). Peter says 'He himself bore our sins in his body on the tree' (1 Peter 2:24), and 'Christ also suffered once for sins, the righteous for the unrighteous, to bring you to God' (1 Peter 3:18).

God's plan was to reconcile sinful humankind to himself through Jesus' death on the cross. The Gospels – Matthew, Mark, Luke and John – show in great detail how he achieved that. Jesus demonstrated that he was the Messiah through his teaching, actions, miracles, and ultimately through his death and his resurrection from the dead. He then gave his great commission to his followers to 'make disciples of all nations, baptising them in the name of the Father and of the Son and of the Holy Spirit, and teaching them to obey everything I have commanded you' (Matthew 28:16–20).

The mission of the church

The task of the church, and the role of all Christians, is thereby to be Jesus Christ's witnesses by demonstrating the reality of God's kingdom here and now and to call others through words and personal example to repentance, faith and full obedience (Matthew 28:19–20). Jesus' death and resurrection provided the means of reconciliation. This wonderful gift is offered to everyone who will put their trust in him, believing and acting on his teaching and growing to full maturity as Christians. To all who receive Christ, he gives the right to become children of God (John 1:12). He gives them a new nature and the gift of his Holy

Spirit to live within them and enable them to understand his word and obey his commands (2 Corinthians 5:17). The first believers were Jewish but the gospel rapidly spread beyond Jewish borders as many Gentiles (non-Jews) were brought into God's kingdom. The church, composed of believing Jews and Gentiles, is the vehicle through which all the nations of earth are to be blessed.

While on earth, Jesus prophesied that Jerusalem and its temple would be destroyed and that the Jews would be scattered all over the world. In AD 70 this was fulfilled when the Romans destroyed the city and temple. But even more seriously, Jesus clearly taught that there would be a day of judgment when all human beings who have ever lived will stand before God and be sent to one of two destinations: either to the new heaven and new earth to enjoy God forever, or to be excluded from his presence forever in hell. These events are described in Revelation, the final book of the Bible. The ultimate destiny of God's people is to live with God and each other forever with new perfect bodies in a world where there is no longer any death, mourning, crying or pain (2 Corinthians 5:1–10; Philippians 3:21–22; Revelation 21:1–5).

This then is the great biblical story – God's divine drama to rescue broken and rebellious people from their sin and restore us to a joyful and healthy relationship with himself and each other. It is essential that we first understand Christ's mission of salvation before we ask how medicine and health fit into it. During the course of this book we will refer back to this story, and unpack parts of it in more detail. Having found our bearings in this grand narrative and seen the trajectory on which all human history is headed, we are ready to set out and explore the big questions of the human journey.

And it all begins with: What does it mean to be human?

FURTHER READING

- Roberts V. *God's Big Picture*. IVP, 2002
- Stott J. *The Cross of Christ, 20th Anniversary Edition*. IVP, 2006

HUMANITY:
WHAT DOES IT MEAN TO BE HUMAN?

*...what is man that you are mindful of him, the son of man
that you care for him? You made him a little lower than the
heavenly beings and crowned him with glory and honour.
You made him ruler over the works of your hands; you put
everything under his feet: all flocks and herds, and the beasts
of the field, the birds of the air, and the fish of the sea,
all that swim the paths of the seas.*
(Psalm 8:4–8, NIV 1984)

I n 2010, British farmers slaughtered nearly 25,000 cattle and
introduced emergency measures to curb the spread of bovine
tuberculosis, costing the taxpayer £90 million. In response,
government ministers approved the cull of up to 100,000 badgers
thought to be responsible for harbouring the disease. The move
provoked the largest animal rights protest since those over fox hunting
in the 1990s. Dr Brian May, astrophysicist and lead guitarist for the
rock group Queen, set up an e-petition to 'stop the badger cull'.
When over 155,000 people signed, it prompted a parliamentary debate.

Few would argue that animals are not worthy of respect and care
but some people today will go to extraordinary lengths in the fight
to protect them. For some, it's mere sentimentality. But for others
it's a deeply felt and serious ideological conviction that it's wrong
to believe human beings are somehow superior or more important
than animals.

Caleigh's friends were strict vegetarians and were passionate about animal rights. They wrote letters to MPs about factory farming and animal experimentation and looked down on people who ate meat or wore fur. Caleigh believed that caring for animals was part of good Christian stewardship and had a lot of sympathy with their position. But when they got involved in violent protests she wondered if they had got things a bit out of perspective. She was struck by what Jesus said about the value of human beings relative to sheep and sparrows and noted that he cooked fish for his disciples and ate lamb at the Passover. Thinking through these things helped her reach a more balanced view on the relative value of human beings and animals.

Australian philosopher Peter Singer popularised the term 'speciesism' in his 1975 book *Animal Liberation* which many regard as giving the animal rights movement its intellectual basis. In a landmark article titled 'Sanctity of Life or Quality of Life?', published in the influential American Journal *Pediatrics* in 1983, he wrote:

We can no longer base our ethics on the idea that human beings are a special form of creation, made in the image of God...Once the religious mumbo-jumbo surrounding the term 'human' has been stripped away, we may continue to see normal members of our species as possessing greater qualities of rationality, self-consciousness, communication and so on than members of any other species, but we will not regard as sacrosanct the life of every member of our species, no matter how limited its capacity for intelligent or even conscious life may be... If we can put aside the obsolete and erroneous notion of the sanctity of all human life, we may start to look at human life as it really is, at the quality of human life that each human being has or can achieve. [1]

---

1. Singer P. Sanctity of life or quality of life? *Pediatrics* 1983; 72(1) pp. 128–129

To Singer and many influential thinkers like him, humans are nothing but the product of matter, chance and time in a godless universe; merely highly specialised animals. The value of an individual human being is determined by his or her level of rationality, self-consciousness, physical attributes or capacity for relationships. This view has led him controversially to support human embryo research, abortion, euthanasia and even infanticide.

Just animals?

There is an element of truth in what Singer says. Humans are living beings with body structures and physiological functions that are very similar to many other living creatures. In fact we share a large proportion of our DNA – our genetic programming – with chimpanzees.

But the Bible insists that we are different from animals. Human beings are made in God's image (Genesis 1:27). Animals are not. This does not mean that we don't share some characteristics with animals. We do. Both animals and humans are made of flesh and blood out of inanimate matter, 'from the dust of the ground' (Genesis 2:7, 19; Ecclesiastes 3:19–20). Like animals we have body structures and organ systems (anatomy), functions (physiology) and complex cellular activity (biochemistry). What makes us unique is that we're made in God's image.

Throughout this book we will come back again and again to the question: 'What does it mean to be human?' As we think through health-related topics we are forced to realise that we are not talking about veterinary medicine but about human beings who are fundamentally different from all the other beings God created.

It's important to acknowledge here that the Bible does see animal welfare as very important. The Bible says that 'the righteous care for the needs of their animals' (Proverbs 12:10). This is indeed what God himself does (Psalm 36:6, 104:10–18). But Jesus himself also said that people were far more valuable than birds and sheep (Matthew 6:26, 12:12) and on one occasion he sent 2,000 pigs to their deaths in order to restore the sanity of one demon possessed man! (Mark 5:1–20). He caught fish and cooked them for breakfast (John 21:9–13). Jesus taught that human beings were more important than animals. He was, in other words, unashamedly 'speciesist'. Why was that? We get a clue from an encounter between Jesus and some of his opponents, recorded in Mark 12 and Matthew 22.

> When John was 16 his dog Kylie was run over and killed. He didn't know she had followed him across the road and was only alerted by the screech of brakes. When he picked her up off the road she was still convulsing and she died in his arms as he stumbled home. John was devastated and felt personally responsible. He cried inconsolably all night but with his parents' help and support buried her the next day in her favourite place. When he reflected as a Christian on the experience many years later he realised how much getting through it had taught him personally about bearing loss and grief. It also caused him to think about why the loss of his pet had affected him so deeply and made him more sensitive to supporting others through human bereavement.

When the Pharisees (Jewish teachers of the law) tried to trap him by asking whether it was right to pay the imperial tax to Caesar, Jesus asked them to show him a coin. They brought him a denarius, and he asked them, 'Whose image is this? And whose inscription?' When they replied 'Caesar's', he said, 'So give back to Caesar what is Caesar's, and to God what is God's.' The Pharisees' focus is on a coin, but Jesus' comments uncover a much deeper question. If a denarius bears the image of Caesar, then what is it that bears the image of God? Because the thing that bears the image of God belongs to God and must be given to him.

As we shall discover, the Bible tells us that human beings have a special status: They are the pinnacle of God's creation.

Paul's father had been a very successful businessman and was an accomplished and much-loved lay preacher who served his church faithfully for many years. But when he was in his mid-fifties he was forced to take early retirement after a major heart valve operation. Later he suffered a number of tiny strokes as a recognised complication of the surgery. Two decades later he developed a rapidly progressive dementia which robbed him of his memory and led to an unpleasant personality change. Paul tried to cope with this by remembering his father as he once was until a Christian friend who had lost his mother in similar circumstances encouraged him to think of him as he would be after the resurrection. This helped him to cope much better with his father's eventual death.

Made in his image

The Bible begins with the four majestic words, 'In the beginning God…'. Genesis 1 tells us about *who* did *what* and a little about *why*; it does not however satisfy our every curiosity about the *when, where* and *how*. For fuller answers to those questions we have to go to the other 'book' that God has revealed himself in – the book of nature (Psalm 19:1–4). Nature progressively reveals its secrets about God's creation as scientific researchers carefully observe it and, as Johannes Kepler (1571–1630) said, 'think God's thoughts after him'. Among Christians seeking to take the Bible seriously as God's word there are a range of views on questions such as the age of the earth and the role evolution might have played; these are beyond the scope of this book. But in the present context it is sufficient to say that, however we think the creation narrative should be interpreted, it clearly teaches something fundamentally profound about what it means to be human.

At the end of the creation narrative in Genesis 1, after making and shaping the world and filling it with plants and animals, God reaches the crowning point of his work:

Then God said, 'Let us make mankind in our image, in our

likeness, so that they may rule over the fish in the sea and the
birds in the sky, over the livestock and all the wild animals,
and over all the creatures that move along the ground.'
(Genesis 1:26–27)

So it is human beings – both male and female – who are made in the
image of God and who therefore belong to God and should be given
to God. This was the point ironically lost on the Pharisees in Jesus'
encounter over the coin. They had refused to give themselves to
God despite belonging to him. Of course everything in the universe
belongs to God (Psalm 24:1), even Caesar's coins, but in all God's
creation only human beings are made in God's image and have
a special status that no other part of creation enjoys.

Special status

What does being made in God's image entail? The following verses
in Genesis 1–2 reveal that human beings have a special status in six
dimensions. They are representative, spiritual, moral, immortal,
relational and creative.

Representative

Human beings are to represent God on earth and to reflect
something of his glory:

> *God blessed them and said to them, 'Be fruitful and increase*
> *in number; fill the earth and subdue it. Rule over the fish in the*
> *sea and the birds in the sky and over every living creature that*
> *moves on the ground.'*
> (Genesis 1:28)

This is not a licence to exploit and destroy the earth, as some have
mistakenly argued, but a commission to look after the earth and its
creatures and vegetation in the same way that God himself would,
with loving care. Not as asset strippers but as diligent stewards.
Human beings, carrying God's delegated authority, were called to
be responsible, reliable and accountable in their rule over the earth.

Spiritual

Humans are spiritual beings carrying the breath of God: 'The Lord God formed the man from the dust of the ground and breathed into his nostrils the breath of life' (Genesis 2:7). Unlike the animals, as spiritual beings we seek meaning and purpose and ask questions – Who am I? Why am I here? Why pain? Why suffering? Why me? Bible commentator Derek Kidner observes: If *formed* expresses the relation of craftsman to material…*breathed* is warmly personal, with the face-to-face intimacy of a kiss and the significance that this was an act of giving as well as making; and self-giving at that'. [2]

Moral

Human beings, unlike the animals, are given instructions about what they must and must not do (Genesis 2:16–17). We are created with the capacity to make moral choices. There are boundaries for human behaviour. Although, tragically, Eve and then Adam disobey God's command, the very existence of the prohibition about eating from the tree of the knowledge of good and evil confirms that we all have the capacity for moral choice. Like God himself, we are moral beings.

Immortal

Humans are immortal beings. God intended us to live forever. In Genesis 2:17, God introduces death as an unwelcome intruder into God's creation: 'You must not eat from the tree of the knowledge of good and evil, for when you eat from it you will certainly die'. As the biblical testimony bears out, human beings exist beyond death. Death is not the end but a gateway to an encounter with God our creator and judge and then one of only two possible destinies.

Relational

Humans are relational beings: 'It is not good for the man to be alone. I will make a helper suitable for him' (Genesis 2:18). Western culture is becoming ever more individualistic, self-centred and narcissistic. But human beings were made to live in relationships: in families and communities. As the poet John Donne (1572–1631) so poignantly reminded us, 'No man is an island'.

---

2.   Kidner D. *Genesis: An introduction and commentary*. London: Tyndale Press, 1967, p.60

Note how in Genesis 1:26 God says 'Let us make man in *our* image...'. God himself is one God, but exists in three persons – Father, Son and Holy Spirit. In the very first verses of Genesis we are introduced to God (the Father) who created the heavens and the earth by means of his Word (Jesus), and that his Spirit (the third person in the trinity) hovered over the water. God himself exists in relationship and has made us for relationship with him and with each other.

Creative

Finally, like God, humans are creative. The first job human beings were given in the Garden of Eden was to name the animals (Genesis 2:19). This process of naming is the basis of taxonomy (the classification of plants and animals) and the beginning of science. Imagine the creativity and influence involved in going from aardvark to zebra! Later in Genesis 4:20–22 we read of human beings domesticating animals, building tents, making musical instruments and developing tools and technology. This creativity is not programmed like that of bees or beavers, but free, expansive, individualised and godlike. Not only is every human being gifted, but each human being has different creative gifts.

Secular models of humanity

The secular world has developed many different models for human beings. *Psychoanalytical* models like that of Sigmund Freud (1856–1939) see human beings as the product of a complex reaction between super-ego, ego and id. The self (ego) is said to be engaged in a tug of war between the demands of conscience (super-ego) and its animal desires (id) creating a conflict which needs to be resolved. *Behaviourists* like B F Skinner (1904–1990) see human beings as complex stimulus-response machines. Human behaviour is shaped by reward and punishment, pleasure and pain. Then there are the *anthropologists* who see humans as simply clever monkeys, or as anthropologist Desmond Morris (b. 1928) termed it, 'naked apes'. Finally we have the *biochemists* who see humans as a series of complex chemical reactions, the product of matter, chance and time in a universe without meaning or purpose. Even consciousness and reason are simply the product of electrochemical impulses.

These are all 'reductionist' models; they assert that humans are nothing but the sum of their individual parts. There is of course an element of truth in all of them. Doctors, scientists and psychologists draw on these models in seeking to understand how human beings function. Biochemistry, physiology and anatomy are important because human beings are physical entities. Psychology, social anthropology and sociology are also relevant because human beings are more than just physical entities – they need to be understood as thinking entities existing in relationship. Philosophy and religion exist because human beings ask deep questions about morality, purpose and destiny. Human beings are also spiritual. We are physical, social and spiritual beings but none of these elements describes us exhaustively and they cannot be separated.

Spirit, soul and body

The Bible teaches that human beings are a complex unity of spirit, soul and body; and that these elements together form an inseparable whole. When Paul talks about 'your whole spirit, soul and body' (1 Thessalonians 5:23) he is really saying 'your whole self'. We can be understood in physical terms because we are made from physical elements, but we are more than just physical beings, more than just bodies. We have souls and spirits too, and these three parts of our natures – spirit, soul and body – interact in a complex fashion. These notions are fundamental to a proper understanding of health and wellbeing. We know that our physical health has profound effects on the way that we think, and that illness causes us to ask questions about meaning and purpose. We know that the mind can also affect physical health in the case of psychosomatic illness. We know that major life events like bereavement or divorce can have profound effects on our health. If doctors treat their patients simply as physical bodies they do them a gross disservice.

It is true that people have physical bodies and that they may need their biochemistry corrected, their physiology normalised and their anatomy realigned. However, human beings are also souls enmeshed in a complex set of relationships and spirits asking serious questions about hope, meaning and destiny. These factors have profound implications for health and need to be addressed too. Theologians wax lyrical over the precise natures of body, soul and spirit and the way they interact, but such detail is far beyond the scope of this short book. Nevertheless the biblical picture is that human beings are not bodies that have souls, nor souls who have bodies. We are 'ensouled bodies' and 'embodied souls'.

Furthermore, our eternal destiny is to remain this way. When Jesus was raised from the dead he did not come back as a disembodied soul, but as a living human being with a real body. He could be touched. He spoke. He lit fires and made beach barbecues. He ate fish. He was recognisable as the same Jesus his disciples had come to know and love. And yet he was also able to appear and disappear at will and enter locked rooms without going through the door. His was a real body, but it was a different kind of body from those we have. Our destiny as believers is to have a body like his (Philippians 3:21; 1 Corinthians 15:35–57; 2 Corinthians 5:1–10) and to live with God in a new heaven and new earth where 'there will be no more death or mourning or crying or pain', where all things will be made new (Revelation 21:1–5).

The image defaced

In the Prologue we noted that the biblical metanarrative (or big overarching story) is in four parts: Creation, Fall, Salvation and New Creation.

In the Fall, human beings reject God's rightful rule, disobey his commands and unilaterally break their relationship with God. Adam and Eve have been granted the freedom of eating of every tree in the Garden of Eden bar one. But they succumb to the serpent's cunning and fall from grace. The serpent first seeks to persuade them that God is unreasonable and restrictive when in fact he has granted them wonderful liberty: 'Did God really say, "You must not eat from *any* tree in the garden"?' (Genesis 3:1, emphasis added).

God, of course did not say this at all, but the woman has already fallen into the trap and twists God's words in her reply: 'We may eat fruit from the trees in the garden, but God did say, "You must not eat fruit from the tree that is in the middle of the garden, and you must not *touch* it, or you will die"' (Genesis 3:2, emphasis added).

God only forbade *eating* from the one tree; touching it was allowed. But then the serpent goes for the big lie: '"You will not certainly die," the serpent said to the woman. "For God knows that when you eat from it your eyes will be opened, and you will be like God, knowing good and evil"' (Genesis 3:4–5). God is thus portrayed by the serpent not just as restrictive but also as having a selfish agenda and protecting his power through deception. So the woman eats the fruit of the tree, as does her husband (who is no innocent or less guilty party, as he was with her at the time and yet did not intervene). The consequences of this act of disobedience are immediate and far-reaching.

When God arrives back in the garden the harmonious relationship has been broken. Confidence and trust have given way to guilt, fear, shame and blame. The man blames the woman. The woman blames the serpent. Both hide from God. The apostle Paul later spells out the cosmic significance of this event: '…sin entered the world through one man, and death through sin, and in this way death came to all men, because all sinned' (Romans 5:12).

In addition to breaking the relationship between God and human beings, the Fall breaks relationships at all levels in creation. Genesis 3:16–19 describe the terrible consequences of sin: the man and woman are now at war, 'Your desire will be for your husband and he will rule over you'. The relationship between human beings and creation is also fractured: 'with painful labour you will give birth to children' and 'cursed is the ground because of you'. There is to be 'painful toil', 'thorns and thistles', 'sweat' and physical death: 'dust you are and to dust you will return'. Work is difficult and frustrating, man has become mortal.

Paradise has been lost, but more than this, human beings are no longer able to exist in close fellowship with God but need to be protected from his glory. They are expelled from the sanctuary of the garden into a world red in tooth and claw, where the serpent, later identified in Revelation 12:9 as the devil himself, will have them and their descendants under his powerful influence. The Fall is complete. Spiritual death has occurred. The perfect relationship is broken and physical death and judgment will follow for the man, the woman and the whole human race.

The stirring of hope

In the depths of this tragedy and ruin there is a glimmer of hope. Adam and Eve are told that the offspring of the woman will one day crush the serpent's head (Genesis 3:15). This is the first reference in Scripture to Christ's coming victory over Satan through his death and resurrection. But we also gain a glimpse of the price that will be necessary to save human beings from their predicament. Adam and Eve are clothed in the skins of animals. These are not only to protect them from the elements and keep them warm. The skins point to the fact that shedding blood will be necessary for their continued protection from God's judgment and to secure their rescue and adoption as his children. This would also be foreshadowed in animal sacrifices, but ultimately fulfilled in the shed blood of Jesus on the cross.

We began this chapter by asking whether humans were 'just animals'; in the vastness of the universe are we just highly developed, but ultimately insignificant organisms? In Psalm 8, David asks a similar question as he looks in wonder at the starry heavens. Echoing parts of our headline passage in Genesis 1:26–28, he is led to ask in humility: 'What is man that you are mindful of him?'

The Genesis account of creation shows that human beings are more than just animals, they are uniquely made in the image of God. But there is another, supremely greater, reason to see humans as special. The Christian physician Thomas Sydenham (1624–1689), known as 'the English Hippocrates' and 'the father of English medicine', wrote that 'We may ascertain the worth of the human race since for its sake

God's only begotten Son became man and thereby ennobled the nature that he took upon him'. In the incarnation, God himself took on human flesh to rescue and become reconciled to human beings. This has huge implications; Professor John Wyatt, a specialist in the care of newborn babies, writes, 'Christians treat the human body with special respect. Why? [because] this is the form in which God became flesh!' [3]

When Jane first ventured into a neonatal unit as part of her nursing training she was repulsed by the appearance of the 'skinny and scraggy' premature babies and wondered whether all the time and money spent caring for them was a waste of resources that could be used better elsewhere. But she was struck by the compassion and care shown by the more senior staff and the devotion of the parents. As she witnessed first-hand what a difference the treatment made and saw families and their babies come through the experience her attitudes began to change and she gradually came to love and respect these little ones as precious creations of God. She later specialised in neonatal care.

Jesus was fully human. He took on our human existence in all its frailty. Jesus was a baby in the womb who went through the trauma of birth and had to be wrapped up to protect him from the cold. He had a body like ours that became tired, felt hunger and thirsty and experienced pain – a body that would ultimately bleed and die. He felt the full range of human emotions too: joy and sorrow, love and compassion, astonishment and anger. In the garden of Gethsemane he was 'overwhelmed with sorrow to the point of death' (Matthew 26:37). He 'wept over Jerusalem' (Luke 19:41). At Lazarus' death we're told that he was 'deeply moved in spirit and troubled' (John 11:33). Jesus shared our nature and in doing so gave a unique and special status to human beings.

---

3.   Wyatt J. *Matters of life and death: Human dilemmas in the light of Christian faith.* Nottingham: IVP, 2009, p.77

Human beings are special because they are made in God's image and because God himself became a human being. This is the basis from which we will build in the coming chapters as we seek to build a biblical understanding of health that will enable us to face the issues of the 21st century.

FURTHER READING

- Barratt H. Regarding the image. *CMF Files* 46, 2011 *bit.ly/1ouFUYG*
- Berry C. The human genome. *CMF Files* 11, 2000 *bit.ly/1oyBnEE*
- Campbell M. The family and bioethics. *CMF Files* 38, 2009 *bit.ly/1oyBnED*
- Fergusson A. What does it mean to be human? in *Hard questions about health and healing*. London: CMF, 2005 *bit.ly/1dxcTe1*
- Jones P. Animal experimentation. *CMF Files* 2, 1998 *bit.ly/ZqVPl6*
- McFarlane G, Moore P. What is a person? *CMF Files* 10, 2000 *bit.ly/1oyBqAk*
- Misselbrook D. Speciesism. *CMF Files* 26, 2004 *bit.ly/1oyBqAh*
- Sipos A. Autonomy: Who chooses? *CMF Files* 29, 2005 *bit.ly/1oyBnEB*
- Wyatt J. Biblical perspectives on humanness in *Matters of life and death*. Nottingham: IVP, 2009 *bit.ly/173frat*
- Wyatt J. Quality of life. *CMF Files* 30, 2005 *bit.ly/1oyBqAi*
- Wyatt J. What does it mean to be a person? *Nucleus* 2004; Spring pp. 10–15 *bit.ly/1vuXmDX*

CHAPTER 2

START OF LIFE
WHEN DOES LIFE BEGIN?

For you created my inmost being; you knit me together
in my mother's womb.
I praise you because I am fearfully and wonderfully made;
your works are wonderful, I know that full well.
My frame was not hidden from you when I was made
in the secret place,
when I was woven together in the depths of the earth.
Your eyes saw my unformed body; all the days ordained for me
were written in your book before one of them came to be.
(Psalm 139:13–16)

I n the previous chapter we saw that human beings are valuable because they are made in the image of God and because God himself took on human flesh in the person of Jesus Christ to pay the price for our sins. This is wonderful, but from what point does that value exist? When does a unique, personal, individual human life begin?

People take different views on this key question. Imagine four people discussing the issue: The first says, 'I believe life starts from the moment of conception. When the egg and the sperm have fused, there is a unique, brand new individual, and all other things being equal, nine months later a baby will be born.'

'I'd like to be a little more agnostic than that' says another. 'Lots of fertilised eggs fail to implant in the womb, and are lost in the woman's menstrual blood flow so she never knows anything about it.

Life can't begin before implantation, and it may even be later…'

'Nonsense', says a third. 'Life doesn't begin until the first breath. Until then the baby is dependent on the mother and not a life in its own right.'

'You're all wrong' says the oldest, with a twinkle in his eye. 'Life begins when the children have left home, and the dog has died.'

The question is crucially important because medical decisions affecting so many of us depend on the answer.

Life or death

The most obvious area of application is abortion. Is the baby before birth just an assembly of cells or is it a living human being worthy of respect? Or does it depend on how developed the baby is? These are questions that evoke strong emotions because the various answers have such strong practical and personal implications. They therefore need to be faced sensitively and with compassion, but they also require clear thinking. We need both warm hearts and cool heads.

The question is equally relevant to a whole host of other issues. Abortion is only really possible after six weeks' gestation because pregnancy is not usually recognised until that point, although biochemical tests might well establish it earlier. But many other medical procedures involve or lead to the destruction of early human embryos. For example, there is some evidence to suggest that some forms of contraceptives (eg the Intra-uterine Contraceptive Device, also known as 'the coil', and the morning after pill) may act by preventing an early embryo from implanting in the wall of the womb.

Pre-implantation genetic diagnosis (PGD) involves removing a single cell from an embryo after fertilisation to test for various genetic abnormalities. Any embryos which carry the mutations are then discarded.

Graham and Ros already had three teenage children and were both shocked and surprised when Ros became pregnant again in her early forties. However their concerns deepened considerably when a screening test revealed the possibility of their baby having Down's Syndrome. Hospital staff encouraged Ros to have a test to settle the matter but Ros was concerned about the risk of miscarriage. She felt very uncomfortable about the suggestion that she might proceed to an abortion were her baby found to be affected. After much agonising thought and prayer they decided not to have the test. If their baby was born with a disability God would give them the grace to love and care for it as a member of their family. As it transpired their little boy was not affected but they were glad in retrospect that they had been forced to confront the issue and were able to help friends with a similar decision later.

Embryonic cloning and some 'mitochondrial replacement' techniques involve destroying one embryo and replacing its nucleus with a nucleus from another individual. Producing some forms of animal–human hybrids also involves the destruction of human embryos.

Many embryos have been used in research to develop treatments for infertility and many in vitro fetrilisation (IVF) programmes still involve producing surplus embryos for research, for donation to other couples or to freeze for future use. Many of these embryos are never implanted into a woman.

These various techniques have become legal and acceptable in Britain as a consequence of the two Human Fertilisation and Embryology Acts of 1990 and 2008. These pieces of legislation effectively gave statutory force to the Warnock Report of 1984 which stated that the human embryo had 'special status' but fell short of saying that it was a human life with rights. But the fact that something is legal does not necessarily make it right in God's eyes. Christians therefore need to think through these issues from first principles rather than just adopting the prevalent cultural view.

Dramatic changes

Over eight million abortions have been carried out in Britain since the Abortion Act came into effect in 1968. There are currently almost 200,000 abortions a year in Britain with 98% of them on grounds of protecting the mental health of the mother. In practice this can range from serious mental health problems through to the usual stresses of an unplanned pregnancy. So, it's perhaps not at all surprising that most people don't give the destruction of human embryos much thought. If abortion is acceptable at eight weeks, then what objection can there be to the destruction of embryos at a few days old and far less developed?

However this has not always been the case. When we consider that virtually all abortions and embryo destruction in Britain to date have been carried out by doctors, many are surprised to see how dramatically medical views on these issues have changed over the last few decades. Not many people know that abortion is against historic codes of ethics like the Hippocratic Oath, the Declaration of Geneva (1948) and the International Code of Medical Ethics (1949) or that in 1947 the British Medical Association called abortion 'the greatest crime'.

The Hippocratic Oath is an oath historically taken by physicians swearing to practise medicine ethically and honestly. It is widely believed to have been written either by Hippocrates (c.460–c.370 BC), a Greek physician often regarded as the father of Western medicine, or by his students. The oath, which dates from around the fifth century BC, is the most widely known ancient Greek medical text and includes the resolution, 'I will not give to a woman a pessary to produce abortion'.

This was the mainstream view until well into the twentieth century. The Declaration of Geneva (1948) states 'I will maintain the utmost respect for human life from the time of conception, even under threat' and the International Code of Medical Ethics (1949) affirms that 'a doctor must always bear in mind the importance of preserving human life from the time of conception until death'. These codes were drafted by doctors after the Second World War in response to some of the atrocities carried out by doctors during the Holocaust. In the same spirit, the UN Declaration of Human Life (1948) asserts that 'everyone has the right to life' and the UN Declaration of the Rights of the Child (1959) affirms that the child 'needs special safeguards and care, including appropriate legal protection, before as well as after birth'.

When the legal abortion rate soared worldwide in the second half of the last century, the World Medical Association was left with the choice of either changing its behaviour or rewriting its ethics. It opted for the latter. In 1970, it adopted the Declaration of Oslo. This endorsed 'therapeutic' abortion in circumstances 'where the vital interests of the mother conflict with those of the unborn child'. Although affirming the need for 'the utmost respect for human life from the time of conception' as laid out in the Declaration of Geneva, it was recognised that there was a 'diversity of attitudes towards the life of the unborn child'. The Declaration of Oslo went on to say that 'where the law allows therapeutic abortion to be performed...and this is not against the policy of the national medical association' then 'abortion should be performed' under certain provisos. The Oslo declaration thus laid the framework for doctors to perform abortions if their 'individual conviction and conscience' allowed it and the law and the national medical association were not in disagreement.

Today, even many doctors are not aware of these documents or the way they have subsequently evolved. But national codes and guidelines – like those of the British Medical Association and General Medical Council in Britain – have come to reflect them. The Declaration of Geneva and the International Code of Medical Ethics have since both been amended to fit in with this new norm. As a result it is estimated that there are now about 43 million abortions carried out worldwide every year.[1] When we consider

---

1.   Facts on induced abortion worldwide. WHO, 2012 *bit.ly/1w5JvTo*

that there are only 57 million human deaths each year from all other causes it becomes apparent what a huge number of abortions this is.

This change in doctors' views has been mirrored in the views of the general population. The public conscience has shifted, not just in Britain, but throughout most of the Western World. Many now take the view that human value, like human life itself, is something that develops gradually, and different people choose to draw the line of humanity at different points. This so-called 'gradualist approach' has similarities with the view of human value Peter Singer espouses (discussed in chapter one). Singer has argued that embryos, fetuses and perhaps even babies with special needs are not persons with rights because they do not have 'higher' brain function.

Starting points

As mentioned briefly at the start of this chapter, different people choose to draw the line marking the beginning of human life – or the point at which life should be fully respected – at different points. Let's look at some of the different positions in more detail:

Fertilisation

Fertilisation is the point when the genetic material from the father's sperm and the mother's egg successfully fuse, and a new, genetically unique individual has come into being. Some argue that fertilisation is itself a process given that the sperm nucleus fuses with the egg nucleus some time after penetrating the egg's surface. However the moment when the 'winning' sperm penetrates the egg, shutting the door against any other sperm entry, is nonetheless the start of the whole process that follows.

Implantation

The fertilised egg passes along the Fallopian tube connecting the ovary to the body of the uterus. Rapid cell division takes place as the embryo develops; the early embryo then implants in the wall of the uterus (womb) – usually at around seven to ten days after fertilisation. By this time measurable hormonal interchange is taking place between embryo and mother and the physiological changes of pregnancy start. The pregnancy test also becomes positive. At this stage, the embryo consists of hundreds of cells and is shaped rather like a tennis ball with a hollow centre. Some embryos fail to implant, but it is very difficult to know how many because the free-floating embryo does not produce measurable chemical substances, and embryos lost in the woman's menstrual blood flow are virtually impossible to detect. Accordingly, estimates of failure vary widely.

Nervous system

The UK Parliament's Warnock committee chose 14 days as the latest time that experimentation could be carried out on a human embryo on the basis that this is the stage by which the neural crest, the part of the embryo which will become the brain and nervous system, has formed. Those who emphasise the capacity for consciousness as being essential for 'life' view this time as the earliest from which life begins.

Organ development

Others opt for when the heart begins to beat. This is about four weeks after fertilisation. Three weeks later, all the main organs are in place and, looking distinctly human, the embryo is now conventionally known as a fetus.

Quickening

This quaint medieval word (still echoed in some liturgies with 'the quick and the dead') describes the sensation the woman feels of her baby moving within her – usually around 18 weeks in the first pregnancy and perhaps a couple of weeks earlier in subsequent pregnancies. We can understand why a woman feels there is now life within her, but modern ultrasound scans, and especially three dimensional scans which also show movement, have taught us that the preborn baby is vigorously active many weeks before this even though these movements cannot be felt by its mother.

Viability

Still others emphasise the point at which a baby is 'viable', meaning it can survive outside the womb. This age of viability has come down with the development of neonatal intensive care but is generally accepted to be at about 23 to 24 weeks.

First breath

As mentioned above, and in spite of our growing understanding of life in the womb, some still believe that the first breath is the moment of the beginning of real human life – 40 weeks after fertilisation. Some have even suggested that permission to live should only be granted to the newborn once they have passed certain tests of human capacity.

What does the Bible say?

How are we to approach the question of life's beginning biblically? Does the Bible, for example, give any support to the idea that some human lives are worth more than others? The Bible clearly teaches that God himself is completely just and impartial (2 Chronicles 19:7). It is therefore not surprising that Jesus and the apostles warned against discriminating against people on the basis of wealth (James 2:3–4), sex, race, social standing (Galatians 3:28) and age (Matthew 19:14). In fact, turning to the Old Testament we find what some have called a 'bias' towards those groups of people who are particularly vulnerable to exploitation or abuse. There was special respect and protection for easily exploited groups such as the poor (Proverbs 22:22–23), widows and orphans (Exodus 22:22–24), foreigners (Exodus 22:21), those with special needs (Leviticus 19:14), slaves (Exodus 21:2–6) and the elderly (Leviticus 19:32).

The Bible simply does not support the view that some human lives are worth less than others. All are made in the image of God and all are equally precious. Devaluing or discriminating against any group of human beings is therefore inconsistent with God's justice. He does not show partiality. The heart of Christian ethical teaching is that we must love as Christ himself loved (John 13:34), that the strong should make sacrifices for the weak and if necessary lay down their lives for the weak (Philippians 2:5–8, Romans 5:6–8). So to suggest that the weak might be sacrificed in the interests of the strong is simply not biblical morality. These texts refute the idea that some human lives are of more value than others.

But can the human embryo and fetus be classed as vulnerable human life? To answer this question we need to turn to references in Scripture to human life before the time of birth.

Fearfully and wonderfully made

Perhaps the most famous passage is Psalm 139. The psalmist, looking back to the beginning of his own life declares:

> *For you created my inmost being; you knit me together in my mother's womb.*
> *I praise you for I am fearfully and wonderfully made; your works are wonderful...My frame was not hidden from you when I was made in the secret place...your eyes saw my unformed body. All the days ordained for me were written in your book before one of them came to be.*
> (Psalm 139:13–16)

The late Rev Dr John Stott (1921–2011) argued in his seminal book *Issues Facing Christians Today* (first published 1984) that this passage affirms three important things about the human life before birth.

First, it affirms that the preborn baby is God's *creation*. God knitted the psalmist together. The Hebrew word used by the psalmist for 'knit' (other versions translate it as 'weaved') is *roqem*, a comparatively rare word in the Old Testament, which is used almost exclusively in texts that describe the curtains and veils of Israel's wilderness tabernacle and the garments of the high priest. To say that an unborn child is '*roqem*' is therefore to say something about the cunning skill of the weaver and about the beauty of his fabric. The tabernacle was the place where the presence of God dwelt. The high priest acted as the mediator between God and man and was the only one able to enter the Holy Place. He also pointed forward to Christ, the true mediator and great High Priest to come who would deal with our sins once and for all (Hebrews 7:26–28). With its allusions to the '*roqem work*' of the tabernacle, the psalm implies not only that God has made the infant in the womb, but also that the infant is being woven into a dwelling for God himself.

Next, the psalmist affirms that God is in *communion* with the preborn baby. At this stage the baby in the womb can 'know' nothing and may not even be aware of its own existence. But this is not important. The key point is that God knows it. It is God's love for the psalmist during his time *in utero* that gives him significance. We see echoes of John's first epistle here, 'This is love: not that we loved God, but that he loved us and sent his Son as an atoning sacrifice for our sins' (1 John 4:10). God's relationship with the baby is a relationship of grace to which the baby itself contributes nothing. It is not its own attributes that give it value. It is the fact that God knows and loves it.

Finally, the psalmist affirms the *continuity* between life before and after birth. The baby in the womb is the psalmist himself, the same person, not a different person and not a non-person. This is supported by the New Testament using the same Greek word *brephos* (child) to describe both John the Baptist in the womb and Jesus Christ after birth (see Luke 1:41, 44, 2:12, 16).

These three themes of *creation*, *communion* and *continuity* are seen in many other Old and New Testament passages.

Called before birth

God calls the prophets Isaiah and Jeremiah *before* birth (Isaiah 49:1; Jeremiah 1:5) and before they are capable even of hearing or understanding his call. He forms Job 'in the womb' as well as bringing him out of it (Job 10:8–9, 18–19). The Isaiah reference above is particularly noteworthy because it comes from one of the so-called 'servant songs' and therefore speaks prophetically of Christ himself. Jesus was also called from the womb. [1]

---

1.   Many other references to life before birth in the Bible reinforce these principles, eg Psalm 51:5, 71:6, 119:73; Ecclesiastes 11:5; Isaiah 44:2, 24, 49:5; Hosea 12:3; Matthew 1:18; Luke 1:15, 41–44.

In Genesis 25:22–23, Esau and Jacob wrestle in the womb, displaying the beginning of the competitive and combative behaviour that would later characterise their family life. David talks about being 'sinful from the time my mother conceived me' and says that God taught him 'wisdom in the inmost place' (Psalm 51:5–6). In Psalm 22:9–10 David again speaks of relationship with God from the beginning of life: 'Yet you brought me out of the womb; you made me trust in you, even at my mother's breast. From birth I was cast on you; from my mother's womb you have been my God'. This psalm also looks forward prophetically to Christ. Jesus' suffering is clearly foretold in the psalm and he actually quotes its words from the cross to emphasise that his death was the fulfilment of its prophecy (Psalm 22:1). The Genesis passage, relating Esau's struggle with Jacob, reminds us that Jesus is the new Israel. Jesus was also the direct descendant of Jacob, later renamed Israel.

Jesus was made like us

Although the Bible does not explicitly distinguish between early biological events like fertilisation and implantation, there are over 60 references which mention 'conception', underlining their importance (eg Genesis 16:4, 29:33–35, 30:7, 19, 38:4). In Matthew 1:20 an angel tells Joseph, referring to Mary the mother of Jesus, that 'what is conceived in her is from the Holy Spirit'. Particularly striking are the verses describing Jesus' conception and intra-uterine development in Luke 1. Here we see Elizabeth, the mother of John the Baptist, prophesying over Christ in his first month of gestation, and the baby John 'leaping' in her womb. The timing is given in some detail. It was in the sixth month of Elizabeth's pregnancy that the angel visits Mary (Luke 1:26). She then goes to visit Elizabeth who gives the prophecy accompanied by her baby leaping (Luke 1:41).

As we have already noted, a baby's movement cannot be felt until about 18 weeks but 'in the sixth month' means, at the very least, 22 weeks gestation. The Scriptures record that, 'Mary stayed with Elizabeth for about three months and then returned home' (Luke 1:51), and that Elizabeth gave birth after that (Luke 1:57).

Given that pregnancy lasts nine months it seems reasonable to deduce from this that Mary left to see Elizabeth almost immediately after the angel's visit. Jesus must therefore have been in the very first few weeks, if not days, of development at the time of the prophecy. The biblical text does not explicitly state that Jesus was conceived (and born) exactly six months after John but this would appear the most natural reading. But if Jesus was not already present in Mary's womb then surely John would not have leapt in Elizabeth's womb.

Why is this relevant? It is important because Jesus' humanity tells us something about our own humanity. We know that in order to act as our substitute on the cross, Jesus had to be 'made like his brothers in every way' (Hebrews 2:17, NIV 1984). He had to be like us in his humanity so that he could take our place. So it would seem to follow that if Jesus was present in the womb in the first month of pregnancy then so were we. Clearly the very beginning of Jesus' earthly life was not exactly like ours (as Mary was a virgin he was not the result of egg and sperm uniting), but in his subsequent development he was fully human just like us.

To deny the humanity of the human embryo would therefore seem to diminish the doctrine of the atonement. In order to die in our place for our sins Jesus had to be fully human like us. He had to be crucified as a real man. He had to be just like us, but without sin. So if he was present in the womb, as argued above, then we must have been also. Otherwise we would have to argue that Jesus was not human in the way that we are.

Although it does not state it explicitly, the Bible leads strongly towards the conclusion that a human life should be fully respected from the moment it begins. We know from science that conception, the beginning of life, is a process that begins with fertilisation, the point at which a new, genetically distinct human life comes into being. So the question might be asked, 'should we not be giving the human embryo the benefit of any doubt?' This conclusion, of course, has strong implications for our decision making. However, there are some strongly and sincerely held objections to this view which we must consider.

When Sinead was training in gynaecology, she was asked to carry out an abortion on a well-developed baby. But when she put her fingers into the uterus the baby kicked her and she froze, unable to go on. A colleague was called to finish the job. The experience caused her to reflect deeply on the decision she had made to be involved and she decided from that point on that she would never do another abortion. Thankfully her colleagues respected her decision and did not pressurise her to become involved. Later she took up voluntary work in her spare time to help a local charity offering women with unplanned pregnancies alternatives to abortion.

Considering objections

There are several arguments often put forward to show that embryos are not human beings worthy of respect:

Potential

Some argue that human embryos (and even fetuses) are not actual human beings, but rather 'potential human beings'. People who take this view will argue that the embryo/fetus acquires full human status either gradually throughout pregnancy or suddenly at a given point in development. But this leaves us with having to draw a discrete line somewhere between potential and real. The problem with this is that biologically, human development is a continuous process beginning with fertilisation. It does not happen in easily divisible steps but each stage merges seamlessly into the next. It might be argued that the only real differences between a fertilised egg and a full term baby, or indeed an adult, are nutrition and time. There are no discrete points after fertilisation, just a long continuous process. Biologically it has to be said that the early human embryo is undoubtedly human; from the time of fertilisation it has human chromosomes derived from human sperm and egg. It is also alive, exhibiting the characteristics of movement, respiration, sensitivity, growth, reproduction, excretion and nutrition. No medical or biological textbook disputes any of these facts. It therefore would seem far more accurate to speak of the human embryo as a human being in an early stage of development or a potential adult; a human being *with potential* rather than a potential human being. Certainly it has potential, but this is because it is already a human life. 'Potential human being' is a term more accurately applied to egg and sperm.

Rationality

Next are those who argue that human embryos are not human beings worthy of respect because they lack rationality or capacity for relationship. As already noted, this was the thinking behind the Warnock Committee's recommendation of no embryo research beyond 14 days, as the neural crests first form ten days after fertilisation. Others have suggested that breathing movements (12 weeks), or 'quickening' (20 weeks), or even the first breath of air should be the end point. It has even been argued that newborn babies are not persons since they lack 'self-awareness'. But the development of the nervous system, like that of the whole embryo, is a continuous process beginning at fertilisation. Therefore choosing an arbitrary point on this continuum would seem to discriminate between human beings on the basis of the level of neural function. We are back to Peter Singer's view that human beings should be valued on the basis of their neurological capacities rather than being valued simply for being human. What does this say about people with dementia or special needs?

Is discrimination on grounds of the level of higher brain function different in principle from discrimination on the basis of any other biological quality or capacity? Is it really that different from discrimination based on age, sex or intelligence? Our value as human beings does not consist in our capacities or attributes but in the fact that we are human, and thereby made in the image of God. It would follow then that arguing that the value of any human life depends on its place of residence (uterus, Fallopian tube or Petri dish) or degree of independence is discriminating on the basis of characteristics that are not actually morally significant. What I can or can't do, where I reside and how dependent I am are not factors that should determine my value before God.

Survival prospects

Another view is that human embryos are not human beings worthy of respect because they have a good chance of dying before birth from natural causes. People who take this position will point to the fact that many early embryos and fetuses die naturally before implantation or before birth.

This is true, but should the value of a human life depend on its survival prospects? We don't say that refugees in Sudan, flood victims in Bangladesh or AIDS sufferers in South Africa are less important than other human beings simply because they have a high mortality rate. Nor would we argue in any other circumstance that lives of those with a low chance of surviving are somehow more disposable or that we can legitimately intervene to end them actively (we will consider this more in chapter six). The aim of medicine is rather to save and preserve life and to seek ways to improve survival prospects of any vulnerable group. As already argued, no one really knows how many early embryos die as there is no easily measurable biochemical 'marker' for fertilisation, as opposed to implantation. It is only after implantation has taken place that we can prove biochemically (through laboratory tests on measurable hormone levels) that an embryo has formed and is actually present.

Genetic abnormality

Some submit that human embryos are not human beings worthy of respect because many embryos that do implant but do not lead to viable pregnancies have a high incidence of genetic (particularly chromosomal) abnormality. It is certainly true that many miscarriages occur as a result of chromosomal abnormalities. But all of these abnormal embryos have formed from the union of an egg and sperm. Isn't it then more accurate to think of them as human lives with severe handicap, human lives with special needs? We would not argue that people *already born* with special needs are of less value than those without, so why should this same argument hold before birth?

Perceived value

Others argue that in practice we simply do not treat embryos and fetuses in the same way that we treat babies. We don't bond emotionally with them or mourn their loss in the same way. The death of a child is much more devastating to parents than a miscarriage or the loss of an embryo before implantation. Also, can we imagine someone risking their life to save embryos from a burning laboratory? But is the worth of an individual dependent on how much we value them or rather on how much they are valued by God? Every day, children and adults die who no one values or mourns. But we would not argue that they are therefore lives without value. My worth and yours does not depend on how much others value us.

Lack of a soul

Historically some within the church have argued that human embryos are not human beings worthy of respect because embryos don't have souls. But the idea that human beings can be divided into body and soul, with the soul entering and leaving the body at some point, is based on the ancient Greek idea of body and soul being separable entities. This is a notion, as we have seen in the previous chapter, which is without biblical support. While it is true that all human beings survive death and face judgment (Hebrews 9:27), our destiny as redeemed human beings is to be clothed in a 'resurrection body' (Philippians 3:21), not to exist as disembodied souls. The biblical word 'soul' (*nephesh*) includes the body (Genesis 2:7). We are 'embodied souls' or 'ensouled bodies'. The soul and the body belong together.

Counting the cost

We began this chapter by posing the key question, 'when does life begin?' The biblical and scientific evidence seem to point strongly in one direction. The Bible teaches that we should not discriminate against any other human being and that the strong should make sacrifices for the weak. Given the strong biblical testimony about life before birth, this leads us to the conclusion that early human life, from the time of fertilisation, should be treated like all other human life. The developing human being in the womb is also our neighbour: made in the image of God and worthy of the utmost respect, wonder, empathy, and protection. This is the view that the Christian church has taken throughout most of its history. In the face of all this evidence it makes sense, even if we are still in doubt about the status of the human embryo, to err on the side of caution and grant it the benefit of this doubt. This chapter has raised many practical questions that cannot be adequately answered in such a short amount of space, which readers will no doubt wish to explore. Our intention here has been first to establish the biblical principles to provide a basis for action, which can then be worked out in individual issues and circumstances. The suggested reading below grapples with these issues in much greater depth than is possible here.

When George and Susan were unable to have a baby after two years of trying, they sought help through their GP and were referred to an infertility clinic. After tests it transpired that Susan's Fallopian tubes had been damaged by an infection she had as a teenager and were unable to transport the eggs she was producing to her womb. They were offered IVF but were anxious about treatments that involved the production of excess embryos for freezing or research. After sharing their concerns with the hospital staff they were allowed to undergo treatment that involved producing only a very limited number of embryos all of which were transferred to Sue's womb. After two attempts they became the parents of twin girls.

Showing the degree of love and respect to human beings before birth advocated here may, in some circumstances, be very costly for us personally: the woman abandoned by the man who made her pregnant; the mother who learns she is carrying a baby with special needs; the couple who find they are infertile and are wondering which path to take. Christian health professionals may also face situations where their reputations or jobs may be at risk because of their unwillingness to take a step that their colleagues have no moral qualms about.

> When Amy was at medical school one of her student colleagues was asked to assist with an abortion. Amy was accused of being judgmental and seeking to impose her morality on others when she expressed her reservations. Other classmates joined in. This led Amy to re-examine her own views in the light of her Christian faith. She worked through the passages in the Old and New Testaments dealing with life before birth and found her personal convictions about the value of life before birth being strengthened. Talking with older Christian colleagues who had had to make a similar stand helped her to cope better with the peer pressure.

It may be that we find ourselves looking back at decisions we have made in the past and having deep regrets or feelings of guilt. It is a comfort that we do not face these situations alone. This is where the Christian community can offer prayer, support and understanding. Each of us, however we have lived our lives, is a sinner needing God's forgiveness daily and needing to be reconciled with him. We can take comfort knowing that Jesus himself, who entered life as a vulnerable embryo, now walks with us in all our decisions, granting us courage, grace and the opportunity for forgiveness and assuring us that he understands and has already walked the human journey before us.

We find ourselves again at the foot of the cross where he fully paid the price for our sins. By laying down his life, he gave us new life and hope. Jesus also called us to be willing to walk in his own footsteps, and called us to love one another as he loved us (John 13:34–35). It is only by grace that any of us stand.

*In humility value others above yourselves, not looking to your
own interests but each of you to the interests of the others.
In your relationships with one another, have the same mindset
as Christ Jesus: Who, being in very nature God, did not
consider equality with God something to be used to his own
advantage; rather, he made himself nothing by taking the
very nature of a servant, being made in human likeness.
And being found in appearance as a man he humbled himself
by becoming obedient to death, even death on a cross!*
(Philippians 2:3–8)

FURTHER READING

- Engel J. When is an embryo? *Nucleus* 2006; Summer pp.27–34 *bit.ly/1oyByQf*
- Fergusson A, Saunders P. Consequences of abortion. *CMF Files* 35, 2007 *bit.ly/1oyByzV*
- Jones D. The embryo and Christian tradition. *Triple Helix* 2005; Summer pp. 10–11 *bit.ly/1oyBwrB*
- Jones D. Exodus 21 and abortion. *Triple Helix* 2009; Summer pp. 16–17 *bit.ly/1oyByQh*
- McFarlane G, Moore P. What is a person? *CMF Files* 10, 2000 *bit.ly/1oyBqAk*
- Roach J and Taylor P. *Facing infertility: Guidance for Christian couples considering IVF*. CMF, 2014
- Saunders P. The status of the embryo. *Triple Helix* 2000; Autumn pp. 12–13 *bit.ly/1oyBwrF*
- Saunders P. Deadly questions on the status of the embryo. *Nucleus* 1998; Autumn pp. 28–34 *bit.ly/ZqVQFH*
- Saunders P. The moral status of the embryo. *Nucleus* 2006; Summer pp. 17–26 *bit.ly/1oyByzU*
- Ward R. Abortion. *CMF Files* 23, 2003 *bit.ly/1oyByzY*

CHAPTER 3

MARRIAGE & SEXUALITY
WHAT IS MARRIAGE FOR?

Husbands, love your wives, just as Christ loved the church and gave himself up for her to make her holy, cleansing her by the washing with water through the word, and to present her to himself as a radiant church, without stain or wrinkle or any other blemish, but holy and blameless. In this same way, husbands ought to love their wives as their own bodies. He who loves his wife loves himself. After all, no one ever hated their own body, but they feed and care for their body, just as Christ does the church – for we are members of his body. 'For this reason a man will leave his father and mother and be united to his wife, and the two will become one flesh.' This is a profound mystery – but I am talking about Christ and the church.
(Ephesians 5:25–32)

In January 2012, The Archbishop of York, Dr John Sentamu, was quoted in the *Daily Telegraph* as saying that marriage is still the bedrock of a society that promotes love, care and forgiveness in relationships. [1] The previous week, a senior High Court judge, Sir Paul Coleridge, had launched a campaign to promote marriage and fight family breakdown. Sir Paul, a Christian believer who has been married for almost 40 years, said that he was 'unashamedly advocating marriage as the gold standard for couples where children are involved'. [2] He later disclosed that he decided to step down from the bench because of opposition from other senior judges to his stance

---

1.   Archbishop of York: Marriage is still the bedrock of society. *Telegraph*, 12 Jan 2012 *bit.ly/1IZ9IGo*
2.   Judge launches campaign to promote marriage. *Telegraph*, 4 Jan 2012 *bit.ly/1IZ9qKd*

on marriage. [3] In a culture where the marriage rate is declining and living together without marrying has become the norm, these sentiments can come across as old-fashioned, yet Sentamu's and Coleridge's comments were not just based on theological convictions but also sound evidence.

The blessings of marriage

Marriage leads to better family relationships, less economic dependence, better physical health and longevity, improved mental health and emotional wellbeing and reduced crime and domestic violence. These were the (unsurprising) main conclusions of *Why Marriage Matters*, a comprehensive report on the benefits of marriage published in 2011 by the Institute for American Values. [4] Based on a survey of over 250 peer-reviewed journal articles on marriage and family life from around the world, a team of 18 leading American family scholars chaired by Professor Wilcox of the University of Virginia drew 30 conclusions about the positive benefits associated with marriage under five headings. Among these conclusions were:

- Marriage fosters high-quality relationships between adults, as well as between parents and children.
- Children who live with their own two married parents enjoy better physical health, on average, than do children in other family forms.
- Marriage is associated with reduced rates of alcohol and substance abuse for both adults and teens.
- Marriage is associated with better health and lower rates of injury, illness, and disability for both men and women.
- Children whose parents divorce have higher rates of psychological distress and mental illness.
- Married women have a lower risk of experiencing domestic violence than do cohabiting or dating women.

---

3. Judge Sir Paul Coleridge quit because of lack of 'support' over marriage stance. *Telegraph*, 29 Nov 2013 *bit.ly/1pcHBcw*
4. Wilcox WB et al. Why marriage matters: Thirty conclusions from the social sciences. Institute for American Values, 2011 *bit.ly/1jn5wCK*

Stephen and Jane met in their early twenties and fell very much in love, eventually marrying a few years later. Two children arrived in quick succession but with Stephen being so busy working at the bank, and his wife seemingly more preoccupied with the children than their marriage, they began to drift apart. Jane found that Stephen was often home late at night and seemed to have little energy left for their relationship. At the same time Stephen was becoming good friends with a woman colleague at work with whom he shared more deeply than with Jane. He found himself becoming emotionally attached to this person and eventually told his wife who was devastated. They sought help from their pastor when they realised their marriage was threatened. However, Stephen could not distance himself from his work colleague and was eventually persuaded that he should change his job. Over the next few years they rebuilt their marriage with some difficulty but were thankful they had been saved from a painful breakup.

Breakdown Britain

Breakdown Britain, [5] a landmark study published in 2006 by The Centre for Social Justice arrived at similar conclusions. Using extensive evidence-based analysis, it found that the breakdown of marriage and the family was also a key driver of Britain's social breakdown. The percentage of children born outside marriage went from 8% in 1970 to 41% in 2003 to 46% in 2009; lone-parent families have increased by 40,000 per year since 1980. Many of the mental and physical health problems that daily fill GP surgeries, hospital wards and outpatient departments are symptoms of this. The main drivers, the five 'pathways to poverty', all correlate with the collapse of marriages: family breakdown, educational failure, economic dependence, indebtedness, and addiction. Furthermore the five 'pathways' are all interrelated. Children from broken homes are twice as likely to have behavioural problems, perform worse at school, become sexually active at a younger age, suffer depression, and turn to drugs, smoking and heavy drinking. Similarly, a parent who has a serious drug problem

5.   Breakdown Britain: Fractured families. Centre for Social Justice 2006 *bit.ly/1qJ5M7x*

or is addicted to alcohol can exhibit destructive behaviour patterns, which can threaten the quality of life for the other parent and for children, leading in turn to family breakdown.

A later report by the Centre for Social Justice titled *Fractured Families: Why stability matters* [6] revisited the state of family breakdown first highlighted by *Breakdown Britain*. The report found that the problem had continued to worsen, with over 20,000 new lone-parent families forming every year. By the age of 15, almost half of all children in the UK are no longer living with both their parents and a million children have no meaningful contact with their fathers. *Fractured Families* detailed the appalling toll family breakdown can take on children, families, and society at large – in economic cost, but also in human cost. Family instability and breakdown is not just an emotional tragedy for children and families involved; it is also a driver of disadvantage and social exclusion.

It is not just breakdown of marriage that contributes to this societal instability. Cohabitation is also a major factor. Cohabitation refers to living with a partner, but not married to or in a civil partnership with them. In 2012, there were 5.9 million people cohabiting in the UK, double the 1996 figure. Over the same period, the percentage of people aged 16 or over who were cohabiting steadily increased, from 6.5% in 1996 to 11.7% in 2012. This makes cohabitation the fastest growing family type in the UK. [7] A 2011 report on cohabitation by Dr John Hayward and Dr Guy Brandon of the Jubilee Centre, a Christian think tank, concluded:

> *Despite the popularity of cohabitation and its relationship to marriage, it is also the case that marriages that start with a period of prior cohabitation are significantly more prone to divorce than those that do not. Where there has been a previous cohabitation with a separate person by one or both partners, the likelihood of divorce soars… Couples who never marry are six times more likely to split by the time their first child is five.* [8]

6. Fractured families: Why stability matters. Centre for Social Justice 2013 *bit.ly/1qMGnu3*
7. Short report: Cohabitation in the UK, 2012. Office for National Statistics, 2012 *bit.ly/1wlLhBa*
8. Haywood J and Brandon G. Cohabitation: An alternative to marriage? Jubilee Centre, 2011, p. iii *bit.ly/ZXLlo5*

The research followed on from the think tank's 2010 publication *Cohabitation in the 21st Century*,[9] which noted that the cost of family breakdown in Britain (measured in terms of spending on tax and benefits, housing, health and social care, civil and criminal justice, and education) was £41.7 billion, equivalent to £1,350 for every taxpayer each year.

There is more research we could mention about the positive influence of marriage on health and wellbeing, and the negative impact of turning our backs on marriage, but let's turn our attention to what the Bible teaches about marriage and the reasons why God brought it into being.

Marriage was God's idea

Marriage is practised by virtually all societies and cultures. It was originally God's idea and is not just something for Christians but for the entire human race. Genesis 2 describes how God gave marriage as a creation ordinance, long before the calling of Abraham, the establishment of Israel or the birth of the church. It was God who first said that it was not good for man to be alone and who created the unique complementarity of the marriage relationship for companionship, pleasure, procreation and the raising of children – one man, one woman, united for life (Genesis 2:24). Marriage also in this way illustrates Christ's own self-giving abandonment to his bride the church (Ephesians 5:31–32), and points to a greater richness of human relationships beyond the grave of which the very best on earth are but a pale shadow (1 Corinthians 2:9–10). We will return to this theme when we examine marriage's purpose in more detail below. But before we do so it is essential to emphasise a crucially important point.

The fact that marriage is a good creation of God does not mean that everyone should get married. The apostle Paul, who quite possibly was never married, is a powerful demonstration of how a single life can be wonderfully complete and a channel of great blessing to others.

---

9. Hayward J & Brandon G. Cohabitation in the 21st century. Jubilee Centre, 2010 *bit.ly/WRYqSQ*

63

He personally chose celibacy for the sake of the gospel and in
1 Corinthians 7 he extols the benefits of singleness for some kinds
of Christian ministry and the important roles of single people in the
church. Even more obviously, Jesus Christ himself never married.
Single people are a huge asset to the church and have a pivotal role
to play in its life and ministry. But our focus in this chapter is not
singleness but marriage.

So let us tease out the essence of the marriage relationship and its
benefits for the health of individuals and society. Ephesians 5 lays
out very clearly the answer to the three crucial questions about the
marriage relationship; its purpose, pattern and practice.

The purpose of marriage

Let's look at what the Bible says about the purpose of marriage.

Companionship

After the creation of man, God declares, 'It is not good for man
to be alone' (Genesis 2:18). Marriage is the most intimate form of
companionship, where two people are able to support each other,
draw strength from each other and to share every aspect of their
lives. In the familiar words of the writer of Ecclesiastes, 'Two are
better than one… If either of them falls down, one can help the
other up… Also, if two lie down together, they will keep warm'
(Ecclesiastes 4:9–11).

Intimacy

Marriage provides the context for sexual intimacy and pleasure. The
Song of Solomon is an erotic love poem, a story of love, courtship
and marriage where the man and woman take emotional and physical
delight in each other. It is full of the most delicate and subtle imagery,
as are all the best love poems. When the beloved wife says, 'Let my
lover come into his garden and taste its choice fruits' (Song of
Solomon 4:16), she is not inviting him to a picnic! Sex within marriage
is to be enjoyed and celebrated. God himself designed sex to be
wonderfully pleasurable and satisfying: 'May you rejoice in the wife of

your youth. A loving doe, a graceful deer – may her breasts satisfy you always, may you be intoxicated with her love' (Proverbs 5:18–20).

Reproduction

Marriage provides a stable environment for bringing children into the world. God's first command to humankind was to 'be fruitful and increase in number' (Genesis 1:28). God's genius in linking reproduction to sex means that children are a product of this most intimate human act. As well as guaranteeing the future of the human race, the biology of the process means that the children carry the genes of both parents in equal measure and so bring together two family lines. 'Sons are a heritage from the Lord, children a reward from him… Blessed is the man whose quiver is full of them', says the psalmist (Psalm 127:3–5). 'Your wife will be like a fruitful vine… your sons will be like olive shoots round your table…may you live to see your children's children' (Psalm 128:3–6).

Child rearing

Marriage creates a nourishing environment for child rearing. The Old and New Testaments are full of advice about how to bring them up. Every Jewish parent knows the *Shema* and the responsibilities of parenthood, 'Impress [these commandments] on your children' (Deuteronomy 6:4–9). Christian parents have the prime responsibility of ensuring that their children know, understand and apply what the Bible teaches in daily life. As the writer of Proverbs echoes, 'Start children off on the way they should go, and even when they are old they will not turn from it' (Proverbs 22:6). This theme is strong in the New Testament too: 'Fathers, do not exasperate your children; instead, bring them up in the training and instruction of the Lord' (Ephesians 6:4). Any widow, in order to receive support from the local church, had to be known for being 'faithful to her husband' and 'well known for her good deeds, such as bringing up children' (1 Timothy 5:9–10).

Security

Marriage provides security for marriage partners and family members. One of the key functions of marriage is to domesticate men and help them wake up to their responsibilities to care for others(!). They are to be advocates for their wives and children, protect them from harm or abuse and support them through times of economic dependence. Sadly, widespread family breakdown in Western countries means we now look more to pensions and savings to support us in old age. But one of the reasons people in developing countries have large families is to ensure that there are plenty of children and grandchildren around to provide support for vulnerable family members. Similarly, in the New Testament only those widows who were without extended family support became the responsibility of the wider church (1 Timothy 5:3–15). How much of the money that democratic states spend centrally on social welfare would be required if families, and therefore communities, held together more effectively and provided better support closer to the point of need?

Sanctification

Marriage, through its associated sexual faithfulness and the discipline of caring, promotes sanctification, 'For this is the will of God, your sanctification: that you abstain from sexual immorality; that each one of you know how to control his own body in holiness and honour… For God has not called us for impurity, but in holiness' (1 Thessalonians 4:3–4, 7, ESV). Marriage is a means of grace by which God promotes purity and spiritual growth in his people, 'You shall be holy, for I the Lord your God am holy' (Leviticus 19:2).

All of these purposes of marriage – companionship, intimacy, reproduction, child rearing, security and sanctification – are either health-related or have some bearing on health. But none of these is actually marriage's *central* purpose.

Marriage's central purpose

According to the Bible, there is an even more profound purpose of marriage. Marriage points to Christ's relationship with his people the church. Marriage is the institution that God has chosen to represent and witness to his own commitment to us.

The prophet Isaiah, looking forward to the redemption of Israel and the coming of the Messiah, Jesus Christ, described it in terms of a marriage:

> *You shall no more be termed Forsaken, and your land shall no more be termed Desolate, but you shall be called My Delight Is in Her, and your land Married; for the Lord delights in you, and your land shall be married. For as a young man marries a young woman, so shall your sons marry you, and as the bridegroom rejoices over the bride, so shall your God rejoice over you.*
> (Isaiah 62:4–5, ESV)

In the final act of the Bible, the book of Revelation, describes Christ coming for his redeemed people the church like a bridegroom for his bride:

> *The Spirit and the Bride say, 'Come.' And let the one who hears say, 'Come.' And let the one who is thirsty come; let the one who desires take the water of life without price… He who testifies to these things says, 'Surely I am coming soon.' Amen. Come, Lord Jesus!*
> (Revelation 22:17, 20)

The fullest exposition of this teaching is found in Ephesians 5:21–33. By quoting the verse about marriage from the creation narrative – Genesis 2:24 – it unpacks the mystery that marriage actually portrays the relationship between Jesus Christ and his church:

> *'Therefore a man shall leave his father and mother and hold fast to his wife, and the two shall become one flesh.' This mystery is profound, and I am saying that it refers to Christ and the church.*
> (Ephesians 5:31–32)

The prime function of marriage, according to the Bible, is that it's a living metaphor of Christ's own eternal union with the church. This shows why marriage is so incredibly precious to God. It points to the glorious eternal relationship between Christ and the people he loves and for whom he has given everything. It foreshadows his own eternal union with his people – for companionship, mutual delight, new birth, discipleship, security and sanctification. But unlike marriage, which is temporary as there is no marriage in heaven (Matthew 22:30), Christ's union with his church is eternal.

Human marriage is a pale reflection of the marriage of Jesus Christ to his bride, the church, which will take place at the end of time. As the man leaves his parents to become inseparably linked with his wife, so Jesus left his Father above to come to earth and commit himself to us, his people. As the wife leaves her parents, so the church is called out of the world to become inseparably linked to Christ. As husband and wife become one flesh, so Christ becomes one flesh with his people. He is the head of his body (Ephesians 5:23) and the cornerstone of his living temple (Ephesians 2:19–21). This is how the Bible explains the purpose of marriage. Now let's see what the Bible sets out as the *pattern* of marriage.

The pattern of marriage

We live at a time when marriage has been progressively redefined by society and by the law in various ways. While recognising the strong affection and commitment that may exist in such partnerships our purpose in this book is to explore what the Bible says. The Bible teaches that marriage is an unconditional, lifelong, exclusively monogamous, sexually intimate, heterosexual relationship. Let's unpack this:

Unconditional

Marriage is unconditional. The traditional English marriage service picks up this level of commitment in its lyrical phrasing: 'For better or for worse, for richer, for poorer, in sickness and in health.' Whatever circumstances life may throw its way, marriage continues.

Lifelong

Marriage is lifelong, 'Till death do us part'. God's intention is that marriage should only be broken by the death of either husband or wife: 'For a married woman is bound by law to her husband while he lives, but if her husband dies she is released from the law of marriage' (Romans 7:2). The painful reality of divorce underlines the fact that this was not how marriage was intended to end.

Monogamous

Marriage is exclusively monogamous; there is but one man and one woman. Again in the marriage service, the couple promise to '[forsake] all others and be faithful [to each other] as long as [they] both shall live'. Although polygamy is still practised in some cultures today, God's pattern is clear. Polygamy, although tolerated in Old and New Testament times (but with strict rules of faithfulness), was never endorsed or commanded, and one struggles to think of a single instance where it did not have serious consequences for the families involved in terms of jealousy, favouritism, rivalry, apostasy and family breakdown. The dynamics which operated in Jacob's family, with his two wives, two concubines and 13 children make an illuminating case study. Elders and deacons, who are to serve as examples to the churches, are to be 'the husband of but one wife' (1 Timothy 3:2, 12; Titus 1:6).

Sexually intimate

Marriage is sexually intimate. As the Bible says several times, the two are to become 'one flesh' (eg Genesis 2:24; Mark 10:8). Marriage, whether children follow as an added blessing or not, is consummated through sexual intercourse.

Heterosexual

Finally, and it is necessary to state this even more decisively today with the legalisation of 'marriage' between same-sex couples, *God's design* for marriage is heterosexual. It is one man and one woman, not two men or two women. It's a complementary relationship where both partners are biologically different, two parts of a whole, and fruitful in reproduction only by virtue of their sexual and biological complementarity. Jesus is not the same as his church; the husband and wife are similarly different from each other.

James could never remember a time when he had felt sexually attracted to girls. As he entered his late teens he began to experience feelings of unwanted sexual attraction to boys. He felt profoundly guilty about this but unable to share it with anyone in his family or at his home church. But he was doubly confused when a local pastor, who had conducted some civil partnership blessings in his church, started teaching that what was really important in a relationship was commitment and not gender. He eventually shared his struggles with a youth pastor who helped him understand what the Bible taught and how better to come to accept the way he was. Over time as his relationship with Christ deepened, and having assistance to cope better with his unchanging feelings, he came to accept that a life of celibacy was the only option. With the support of good friends he eventually became a pastor himself and was able to minister effectively to others struggling with similar issues.

When a couple are married, they form an unconditional, lifelong, exclusively monogamous, sexually intimate, heterosexual relationship. The very same biblical definition of marriage was part of British law for centuries and was formally defined in a famous court case late in the nineteenth century. In UK Law, the classic legal definition of marriage dates back to that given by Lord Penzance in the case of Hyde v Hyde in 1866. Marriage, it says, is '…*the voluntary union for life of one man and one woman to the exclusion of all others*.' So there are four conditions for a marriage:

1.　It must be voluntary
2.　It must be for life
3.　It must be heterosexual
4.　It must be monogamous

In addition, the parties must be of marriageable age. Subsequent moves in Britain and elsewhere have watered down and redefined this legal definition to allow for easy divorce and so-called 'same-sex marriage', but human beings cannot change by law what God himself has ordained.

The practice of marriage

Ephesians 5:1–2 provides the overall context in saying to all members of the church, both men and women, 'Be imitators of God…and live a life of love, just as Christ loved us and gave himself up for us' (NIV 1984). Because marriage is a metaphor of Christ's relationship with the church, and based on the pattern described above, the roles played by husband and wife are different. Therefore husband and wife receive different but complementary exhortations: 'Husbands love your wives' and 'Wives submit to your husbands'. The difference is not to do with status because before God there is neither male nor female because all are one in Christ. In the same way there is 'neither Jew nor Greek' and 'neither slave nor free' (Galatians 3:28). People of different race, social status or gender are all one in Christ.

The difference is not to do with divine inheritance either because the Bible is clear that men and women are 'joint heirs' of the gift of life (1 Peter 3:7). Nor has it anything to do with sexual rights. There is equality in sexuality as the wife does not have authority over her body but the husband does. But in like manner the husband does not have authority over his body but the wife does. Their bodies belong to each other. This is the basis on which the apostle Paul says they should 'give' to each other their 'conjugal rights' and not 'deprive one another' sexually (1 Corinthians 7:3–5, ESV). This can be a real test of selflessness as in most marriages the sexual appetites of the respective partners are not the same.

The difference is in role. God has assigned different but *complementary* roles to husband and wife. I recognise that the matter of marriage roles is somewhat controversial even among Bible-believing Christians and that not all share the position I am about to outline. But while respecting that others may take different positions I make no apology for relating what I understand the Bible to be saying.

The husband has a challenging role: he is 'the head of the wife even as Christ is the head of the church' (Ephesians 5:23), and with this role comes grave accountability and responsibility. In his leadership he is not to dominate but serve and sacrifice, always following Christ. The apostle Paul commands husbands to 'love your wives, *just as Christ loved the church* and gave himself up for her' and encourages them to 'love their wives as their own bodies ...after all, no one ever hated their own body, but they feed and care for their body, *just as Christ does the church*' (Ephesians 5:25, 28–29, emphasis added). The question the husband is meant to ask is: how did Christ love the church? He was patient when she failed, he lifted her up when she fell, he sought after her when she strayed, he was gentle, tender and gave himself up for her. Husbands are to give themselves up in a life of loving sacrifice for their wives.

It is in the light of this servant-hearted, sacrificial headship that we must understand the command that the wife 'should submit in everything' to her husband 'as the church submits to Christ' (Ephesians 5:24). The Greek word translated 'submit' (*hupotasso*) is the same word used in Scripture to describe how Christian believers should submit to God, how Jesus submitted to his parents and how citizens should submit to the governing authorities. The wife is called to recognise the role God has given to her husband, not because he deserves it (behind every great man there is an equally surprised woman!), but because God has given him this role. This does not diminish the wife, but rather frees her to grow into her full potential, calling and gifting in Christ. Proverbs 31:10–31 paints a beautiful picture of the 'wife of noble character'. She is not only a wise teacher 'clothed with strength and dignity' who 'watches over the affairs of her household' but also a generous philanthropist and businesswoman who 'sets about her work vigorously' and in whom 'her husband has full confidence'. The fact that God has given her husband the leadership role does not mean that she cannot lovingly challenge or rebuke him; to the contrary, this is part of her duty as a sister in Christ. But she also needs to help him fulfil his role as head and leader by submitting to him in obedience to God.

Note that neither of the instructions to husband or wife are conditional on how the other behaves. Husbands are not to love only if they find their wives lovable – but regardless. Similarly, wives are not to submit only if their husbands are worthy of it – but unconditionally. But if each performs his or her role it will be much easier for the other. Loving husbands are easy to submit to and wives who gently and willingly submit are easy to love. The creation narrative emphasises this beautiful partnership. The famous Bible commentator Matthew Henry (1662–1714) puts it eloquently in his treatment of Genesis: 'The woman was made of a rib out of the side of Adam; not made out of his head to rule over him, nor out of his feet to be trampled upon by him, but out of his side to be equal with him, under his arm to be protected, and near his heart to be beloved.'

This is the Bible's pattern for marriage. And when God's pattern for marriage is followed, God's purposes for marriage are fulfilled, and this provides the seedbed for human flourishing, wellbeing and health. But fallen people living in a fallen world often go astray from this ideal. So let's turn now to look at the impact of departing from God's good design.

Sex outside marriage

What about sex outside marriage? We have deliberately spent the bulk of this chapter laying down the Bible's framework for marriage rather than focusing on the distortions brought about by the Fall, both of the marriage relationship itself and of sexuality. As we have seen, the Bible is full of references to sex and marriage from the first chapter of Genesis to the last chapter of Revelation (Genesis 1:28, Revelation 22:17).

The 'one man, one woman, for life' pattern is an Old Testament creation ordinance, upheld by Jesus and Paul in the New Testament (Genesis 2:24; Matthew 19:3–12; Ephesians 5:22–33). Sex in the context of marriage (Genesis 2:24; Matthew 19:3–12) is viewed as the wonderful gift of a loving creator (Proverbs 5:15–20; Song of Solomon 4:11–16) and a sign of Christ's coming marriage with the church (Ephesians 5:32; Revelation 19:7). But in stark contrast, any sex outside marriage is seen as disastrous. It is profoundly offensive to God precisely because it desecrates Christ's own bond with his church and so is uniquely identified as a sin against the body:

> *Flee from sexual immorality. All other sins a person commits*
> *are outside the body, but whoever sins sexually, sins against*
> *their own body. Do you not know that your bodies are*
> *temples of the Holy Spirit, who is in you, whom you have*
> *received from God? You are not your own.*
> (1 Corinthians 6:18–19)

Andy's parents had split up when he was four and he had grown up without a father. His mother loved him and his sister deeply and did the best she could in bringing them up, but Andy always felt disadvantaged relative to other boys whose fathers were much more involved in their childhoods. He lost interest in school when he was in his mid-teens and got involved with some 'friends' who drank heavily at weekends and were sexually active. Andy had half a dozen or so sexual relationships with girls by the time he was twenty but none seemed to last long. After he became a Christian in his early twenties he was challenged to change his lifestyle and to stop sleeping around. After a few years he became better at building friendships with people of the opposite sex that did not involve anything physical. He met Jo through the church youth group and they got married in their late twenties.

It is striking that the bulk of the Old Testament's specific teaching about sexual immorality is found in Leviticus 18 and 20, because right between these is chapter 19 with its central command, 'Be holy because I, the Lord your God, am holy' (Leviticus 19:1). All wrong patterns imaginable are listed several times in specific detail (Exodus 22:16–19, Leviticus 18:1–30, 20:1–27; Deuteronomy 22:13–30) and include all sex outside marriage: Sex before marriage, adultery, incest, sex with people of the same sex, and sex with animals. Under the Old Covenant almost all these acts carried the death penalty, an indication of how seriously they were viewed by God. It doesn't matter whether there is chemistry or strong companionship between the two people involved nor how badly they may have been hurt by others including even a spouse. All sex outside marriage is wrong.

In the New Testament the more general term 'sexual immorality' (the Greek *porneia* from which we derive the word pornography) is used and the moral standards for God's called and chosen people, the church, are even more demanding than they were for Israel. God's people are to be holy through and through. Not only is adultery wrong, but lust is wrong. Not only must one not divorce, except on grounds of sexual immorality (*porneia*), but 'whoever marries a divorced person commits adultery' (Matthew 5:27–32). Furthermore, while the death penalty no longer operates for sexual sin, those who persist in sexual sin without repentance are at risk of losing their place in God's kingdom:

> *Do not be deceived: Neither the sexually immoral nor idolaters*
> *nor adulterers nor men who have sex with men nor thieves*
> *nor the greedy nor drunkards nor slanderers nor swindlers*
> *will inherit the kingdom of God.*
> (1 Corinthians 6:9–10)

> *But the cowardly, the unbelieving, the vile, the murderers,*
> *the sexually immoral, those who practise magic arts,*
> *the idolaters and all liars – they will be consigned to the*
> *fiery lake of burning sulphur. This is the second death.*
> (Revelation 21:8)

> *Outside are the dogs, those who practice magic arts,*
> *the sexually immoral, the murderers, the idolaters and*
> *everyone who loves and practises falsehood.*
> (Revelation 22:15)

These verses leave us in no doubt: sexual sin is serious! However, it's also clear that *all* sin is serious – sexual immorality is just one form of sin and similar warning needs to be taken about all the other sins mentioned. There is not space here to do full justice to the issue of homosexuality and this issue has been handled well elsewhere (for example, see further reading below), but a few words are necessary. The verses in Scripture specifically dealing with homosexual acts, both male and female, are plentiful and all see it within the bracket of 'sexual immorality' – one of many forms of sex outside marriage which are equally outside God's revealed pattern (Genesis 19:1–29; Leviticus 18:22, 20:13; Judges 19:1–30; Romans 1:24–27; 1 Corinthians 6:9–11; 1 Timothy 1:8–11).

> Jack and Emma met through the church youth group and started going out in their late teens. Over the next few years at university they grew much closer and their relationship grew more physical. They initially felt guilty about their degree of intimacy but as each new step 'felt so good and right' they eventually made the decision to move in together. However, they felt very uncomfortable when the pastor in their new church and some of their friends challenged them about their behaviour. After some careful reflection and a re-evaluation of what the Bible taught they decided to get married. They moved out of the same house and continued their courtship with much clearer boundaries established. They eventually got married but regretted their earlier decisions to go as far as they had.

We briefly touched on cohabitation earlier in this chapter, noting how common it is and also how it falls short of marriage. Although many cohabiting couples are strongly committed to one another and remain faithful, cohabitation is not an option for Christians.

In addition to specific teaching on the dangers of departing from God's pattern, the Bible contains many warnings in the context of stories involving real people.

Cautionary tales

The Bible treats us to some beautiful stories of love and courtship leading to marriage. There is Isaac and Rebekah (Genesis 24), Jacob and Rachel (Genesis 29:16–30), Boaz and Ruth (Ruth 3), David and Abigail (1 Samuel 25) and of course the Song of Solomon. But the Bible is also full of distressing narratives about how sex and marriage can be distorted. There is Shechem's appalling rape of Jacob's daughter Dinah, which leads to retaliatory genocide by Levi and Simeon (Genesis 34). In the next chapter Jacob's oldest son Reuben sleeps with his father's concubine Bilhah, the mother of his brothers (Genesis 35:22). The result of these two incidents, aside from the damage they wreak on family relationships, is that the rights of the firstborn pass to Jacob's fourth son Judah, from whom comes the Messianic line. But Judah's behaviour also leaves much to be desired. He commits adultery with his daughter-in-law Tamar, believing her to be a prostitute (Genesis 38).

Later in Israel's history, a massive orgy between Israel and the daughters of Moab results in the fornication and judicial killing of Zimri and Cozbi (Numbers 25), leading to a plague which kills 24,000 people. The incident later becomes a warning to all Israel given by the apostle Paul hundreds of years later (1 Corinthians 10:8). Then there are the homosexual orgies and attempted, or actual, gang rapes of Sodom and Gibeah described in Genesis 19 and Judges 19 respectively. The latter act leads to the destruction of virtually the entire Israelite tribe of Benjamin in a bloody civil war. It is arguably Israel's darkest period.

Perhaps best known is David's seduction of, and adultery with, Bathsheba, and his wicked attempt to cover up the deed and the unplanned pregnancy resulting from it through lies, deception and finally arranging for the murder of her husband Uriah the Hittite (1 Samuel 11). The disintegration of David's family that followed, his son Amnon's incestuous rape of his half-sister Tamar, Absalom's murder of Amnon and the coup leading to David's flight from Jerusalem and Absalom's death, can be traced as a direct consequence (2 Samuel 13). It triggered disintegration of David's family, which ultimately split his kingdom. The warning from this story and many others like it is very clear. Sex outside marriage is deeply damaging to human relationships and morally wrong. Perhaps this is why King Solomon, a later product of David and Bathsheba's fateful union, spent so much time writing about the consequences of adultery, including three consecutive chapters of Proverbs (Proverbs 5–7). He had lived through it and seen what transpired as a result.

The consequences of sex outside marriage in our own society – ignoring God's purposes and pattern – are epidemic in proportions and have profound effects on health and wellbeing. It can lead to unplanned pregnancies, abortions, sexually transmitted diseases and of course the deep emotional hurt and damage to the ability to form lasting relationships. Sex outside marriage is also a key contributor to family and even societal breakdown, the message with which we began this chapter.

In contrast, the biblical position is that sexual intercourse is for marriage, so having sex with someone is only safe physically, emotionally and spiritually in the context of that exclusive, lifelong covenant relationship. Sexual sin is serious. It diminishes our humanity and demeans us as people – and yet God sent his Son Jesus to die to pay the price for all kinds of sin, and through his atoning death, to make it possible for us to be reconciled to him. However far we may have fallen, there is a way back. And there is a God-given path to follow.

God's grace and forgiveness

We see God's mercy in allowing those who were guilty of serious sexual immorality to live and attain eternal life – Reuben, Levi, Simeon, Judah and David will all be there in the kingdom of heaven, free and forgiven. Furthermore we see God's grace in that he turned around these disastrous situations to enable our salvation to take place. Rahab the prostitute, and the adulterers Judah, Tamar, David and Bathsheba are all included in the ancestral line of Jesus Christ himself. Sexual immorality is a disaster, but God's redemptive love and grace is greater, and the fountain of his mercy deeper and able to wash away the foulest of guilty stains.

Our intention in this chapter has been to review the purpose, pattern and practice of marriage and, from that, to understand that sex outside God's pattern is off limits. This is the framework that will set us on the right path. If we get these basics right and build them into our lives then we are well on the way to resisting sexual temptation, whether it comes in the form of inappropriate relationships or in other ways that we have not discussed, such as through pornography and sexual addiction. So, whether we are married or single, as Christians let's celebrate, demonstrate, promote and protect marriage as the vehicle of blessing that it is for husbands, wives, children, parents, extended families, communities and ultimately the whole world. And let's remember why God invented it and loves it so much.

FURTHER READING

- Curtis H. Teenagers and sex. *Triple Helix* 2002; Summer pp. 6–8 *bit.ly/ZqVSxk*
- Goddard A, Harrison G. *Unwanted same-sex attraction: Issues of pastoral counselling and support.* London: CMF, 2011 *bit.ly/xgYJjS*
- Goddard A, Harrison G. *Biblical and pastoral responses to homosexuality.* London: Evangelical Alliance, 2012 *bit.ly/15lVJgy*
- Saunders P. The blessings of marriage. *Triple Helix* 2011; Winter p. 3 *bit.ly/1oyByzW*
- Saunders P. Homosexuality. *CMF Files* 20, 2003 *bit.ly/ZqVQFG*
- Richards C. Caught in the net. *Triple Helix* 2006; Autumn pp. 8–9 *bit.ly/1oyBwrz*
- Stammers T. Teenage sex. *CMF Files* 37, 2008 *bit.ly/1oyByzX*
- Stammers T. Abstinence education. *Triple Helix* 2003; Spring pp. 10–11 *bit.ly/1oyBwrA*
- Wilson J. Marriage and health. *Triple Helix* 2004; Summer pp. 6–7 *bit.ly/ZqVQFF*

CHAPTER 4

PHYSICAL HEALTH
HOW SHOULD I LIVE?

*Join together in following my example, brothers and sisters,
and just as you have us as a model, keep your eyes on those
who live as we do. For, as I have often told you before and
now tell you again even with tears, many live as enemies of
the cross of Christ. Their destiny is destruction, their god is
their stomach, and their glory is in their shame. Their mind
is set on earthly things. But our citizenship is in heaven.
And we eagerly await a Saviour from there, the Lord Jesus
Christ, who, by the power that enables him to bring everything
under his control, will transform our lowly bodies so that they
will be like his glorious body.*
(Philippians 3:17–21)

Human lifespan is limited

According to the Guinness World Records (at the time of writing) the oldest living person verified by original proof of birth is Misao Okawa, a Japanese woman who turned 115 in 2013.

Many, of course, never reach such an old age before they die, but there does appear to be a natural ceiling to human longevity at around 120 years. After a period of near perfect growth and cell renewal (in humans, between 20 and 35 years of age), ageing is characterised by the declining ability to respond to physical stress, increasing homeostatic imbalance (ability to maintain physiological and biochemical systems) and increased risk of disease. This currently irreversible series of changes inevitably ends in death.

Many scientists now believe that the ageing process is genetically programmed and results from accumulated damage in our DNA. It may be related to a fall in the level of an enzyme called telomerase. Telomerase repairs DNA sequences called telomeres which are located at the end of chromosomes. We know that telomeres shorten throughout life and that this eventually leads to cell death. Also certain premature ageing syndromes have been associated with telomere shortening. But regardless of the actual mechanism of ageing it is interesting that the Bible itself talks of 120 years as the maximum human life span. Before sending the Flood God said: 'My Spirit will not contend with humans forever, for they are mortal; their days will be a hundred and twenty years' (Genesis 6:3).

There is no clear explanation for the vast lifespans recorded in the early chapters of Genesis. Noah himself is reported to have lived 950 years. However, the biblical genealogical records show that ages dropped progressively over several generations after the Genesis Flood to present levels. Methuselah, the oldest man mentioned in the Bible, was 969 and lived before the Flood (Genesis 5:27). Abraham died at 175 (Genesis 25:7) and Moses 120 (Deuteronomy 34:7). This has led people to speculate that human lifespans fell progressively over time as a part of the curse of the Fall (Genesis 3:17–19), and that this was mediated through accumulated genetic defects. It is interesting that some species on earth, unlike man, do not actually demonstrate ageing in the same way. There are creatures whose mortality stays constant throughout their whole life, like hydra or the hermit crab. Their bodies do not seem to degenerate during their lifetime. And then there are even species whose probability of dying decreases as they grow older, like the red gorgonian (a coral), the netleaf oak and the desert tortoise. [1]

---

1. Aging out of bounds: New demographic data show how diversely different species age and biologists cannot explain why. *Max-Planck-Gesellschaft*, December 8 2013. *bit.ly/1u80Qlc*

Psalm 90, attributed to Moses, suggests that human ageing is an expression of God's wrath on fallen humanity:

> All our days pass away under your wrath; we finish our years
> with a moan. Our days may come to seventy years, or
> eighty, if our strength endures; yet the best of them are but
> trouble and sorrow, for they quickly pass, and we fly away...
> Teach us to number our days, that we may gain a heart of wisdom.
> (Psalm 90:10–12)

We are all subject to ageing and should take our mortality seriously in planning how we are to live our lives. It is striking that a life expectancy of 70–80, in healthy societies for those who have survived to adulthood, has not changed that much between Moses' time (about 1500 BC) and the present day. For the period 2005–2010, the worldwide average life expectancy at birth was 68.7 years (66.5 years for males and 71.0 years for females). In the UK it was higher at 79.6 years.[2]

How does this help us? Well, we need to grasp the reality that it is most unlikely that any of us will live beyond 120 years and most of us will probably die between 70 and 90. But this is only an average. It doesn't help us to know what will happen to us personally. Obviously many people die younger than 80 as a result of accidents, violence or disease. All we can say with certainty is that God himself knows, and has set, the length of our life and the day of our death. The psalmist says, 'All the days ordained for me were written in your book before one of them came to be' (Psalm 139:16).

The causes of illness

So what are the common causes of illness that affect life expectancy? Many diseases have an inherited element and we may have been 'dealt a poor hand' in the longevity stakes. But it is God who is sovereign even over so-called chance events like the throw of the dice: 'The lot is cast into the lap, but its every decision is from the Lord' (Proverbs 16:33).

2.   Department of Economic and Social Affairs. United Nations population prospects revision 2012: Highlights and advance tables. United Nations, 2013 *bit.ly/1j2Ub1c*

There are over 6,000 known genetic diseases which vary widely in severity and age of onset. Many cancers also have a genetic element, as does coronary heart disease. Our environment also plays a part. People living in Australia are at greater risk of some forms of skin cancer than those in Lapland. Those in developing countries are far more likely to die of infections than those in the West. Diets have a major impact on health and vary widely between countries and communities. The availability of medical care plays a major role, too. 99% of maternal deaths – almost all of them preventable – occur among the poorest two thirds of the world's population.

Many of the factors that affect our health are things over which we have no control. However, lifestyle choices are something that we have a lot of control over and many people die early as a result of bad decisions. To put it more bluntly, many people in more wealthy developed countries eat, drink and worry themselves to death, or end up with a disease or injury which changes their lives because of how they have chosen to live.

The five big killers

While we can never make accurate predictions for any given individual many of the major causes of death in the UK can generally be delayed or treated, to some extent and may even in some cases be avoidable.

Over 50% of people in the UK will now live to 80, [3] but the five biggest killers account for more than 150,000 deaths a year *among under-75s* in England and Wales each year and the Department of Health estimates 30,000 of these deaths, or one in five, are entirely avoidable. [4] [5] [6] So what are the five big killers in the UK? They are cancer, coronary heart disease, stroke, lung disease and liver disease.

3.   Mortality in England and Wales: Average life span. Office for National Statistics, 17 December 2012 *bit.ly/1meqtYQ*
4.   Murray CJL et al. UK health performance: Findings of the global burden of disease study 2010. *Lancet* 2013;381 pp. 997–1020 *bit.ly/1ixPeqa*
5.   Mortality statistics: every cause of death in England and Wales. *Guardian*, 14 January 2011 *bit.ly/1uHbYNE*
6.   What do people die of? Mortality rates and data for every cause of death in 2011 visualised. *Guardian*, 6 November 2012 *bit.ly/1uGXKOb*

When Carol was 35 she noticed a lump in her breast and had it looked at by her local GP. A mammogram and biopsy confirmed cancer and surgery showed spread to the glands in her armpit. Carol opted for a mastectomy and breast reconstruction and after a course of chemotherapy was doing well five years later. She was thankful for the treatment but also concerned that it hit her so young. After learning that a number of her aunts and her grandmother had also had breast cancer at an early age she was encouraged to have some genetic testing to see whether she carried a gene that had put her at particularly high risk of catching the disease. This being confirmed she had her daughters tested too. They are now recognised as high risk and are having regular screening to ensure that any cancer is detected early.

Cancer is the biggest killer, accounting overall for around 140,000 deaths in England and Wales each year. Six in ten people will get cancer at some time in their lives and just over one in three will die from it. There have been good inroads made into improving outcomes for some of the most common cancers. But it is estimated that about a 20% of cancers are linked to smoking, 10% to being overweight or obese and 8% to alcohol. [7] Also, many cancers are detected too late. Although there are national screening programmes for certain cancers, like breast and cervical, public awareness of symptoms and the need to seek help early is still too low. More than three out of five cancers are diagnosed in people aged 65 and over. It is perhaps not surprising that cancer is the number one fear for the British public, ahead of debt, knife crime, Alzheimer's disease and losing a job.

Coronary heart disease accounted for 64,000 deaths in England and Wales in 2011. More than a quarter of these deaths occurred in people who were younger than 75. Smoking, being overweight and

---

7.   All cancers combined key facts. Cancer research UK. *bit.ly/1ISXubg*

having high blood pressure are all key risk factors. But there are also risk factors over which we have no choice at all: family history (non-modifiable), gender, age and lipid (fat) levels (which increasingly appear to be largely inherited). The key is to change that which we can and accept that which we cannot.

Stroke, accounting for 44,000 deaths per year in England and Wales,[8] is the leading cause of disability. More than 150,000 people have a stroke every year in the UK. Some people suffer a 'mini-stroke' (a stroke-like event, but the symptoms pass within 24 hours), and 10–15% of these go on to experience a full stroke within one month. Thankfully, new research suggests the risk could be cut by 80% if they recognise the symptoms and seek immediate treatment. According to the Stroke Association, if all mini-stroke patients received urgent treatment immediately, this could reduce the number of strokes by up to 10,000 per year.[9]

Lung disease kills about 67,000 people a year in England and Wales and is one of the most common causes of emergency admission to hospital. More than three million people in England are currently living with chronic obstructive pulmonary disease (COPD) and asthma. The most important cause of COPD is smoking, but about 15% of cases in some communities are work-related, triggered by exposure to fumes, chemicals and dusts at work.

Liver disease is the only major UK cause of death still increasing year-on-year and has risen 25% in less than a decade.[10] It accounts for about 7,000 deaths per year in England and Wales. Two of the major causes of liver disease – obesity and harmful drinking – are preventable. The third cause, undiagnosed infection, can also be preventable if it is sexually transmitted or due to injecting drugs. More than a third of men and over a quarter of women regularly exceed the government recommended level of alcohol intake – 21 units of alcohol a week for men and 14 units for women with two

8.   Margaret Thatcher dead: Strokes kill 45,000 people per year. *Huffington Post*, 8 April 2013 *huff.to/1o1sdWt*
9.   After a mini-stroke, immediate treatment can cut stroke risk by 80%. Stroke association *bit.ly/1vZQkF3*
10. Liver disease deaths reach record levels in England. *BBC News*, 22 March 2012 *bbc.in/1o1sg4L*

alcohol-free days per week. There are two units in a standard can of lager, beer or cider and two units in a 175ml glass of wine. [11] Liver disease kills as many people as diabetes and road deaths combined. [12]

Deaths from other causes are far less common. In 2009, there were 6,000 deaths from Alzheimer's, 5,000 from diabetes, 5,000 from Parkinson's disease, 3,000 from kidney failure and 2,000 from road accidents.

Improving our chances

Since it is the biggest killer, what can we do to lessen our chances of developing cancer? Cancer Research UK estimates that more than four in ten cancer cases could be prevented by lifestyle changes, such as not smoking, keeping a healthy body weight, cutting back on alcohol, eating a healthy balanced diet, keeping active, avoiding certain infections (like the sexually transmitted Human Papilloma Virus (HPV)), staying safe in the sun and avoiding occupational hazards like chemicals in the workplace. [13] The world famous US Mayo Clinic [14] in Rochester, Minnesota, gives a similar list of seven tips to lower your cancer risk as follows: [15]

- Don't use tobacco
- Eat a healthy diet (plenty of fruit and vegetables, low fat, moderate alcohol)
- Maintain a healthy weight and be physically active
- Protect yourself from the sun
- Get immunised (especially if at risk for hepatitis B and HPV)
- Avoid risky behaviours (such as unsafe sex and sharing needles)
- Get regular medical care including cancer screening

For Christians who don't smoke, don't have sex outside marriage, don't drink to excess and use sunscreen (!) this could arguably be pruned down to eating a healthy diet, maintaining a healthy weight and staying

11. Recommended safe limits of alcohol. *Patient.co.uk bit.ly/1xO2e57*
12. Facts about liver disease. British Liver Trust *bit.ly/1rjbWXq*
13. Can cancer be prevented? Cancer Research UK *bit.ly/1mphOvf*
14. *www.mayoclinic.org*
15. Cancer prevention: 7 tips to reduce your risk. Mayo Clinic *mayocl.in/Zg9BGk*

physically active. But, having said that, some Christians do engage in sexually immoral behaviour, smoke, drink to excess, or do all three, both before and *after* conversion. It is a sobering thought however, that poor diet, obesity and physical inactivity are major reasons for premature deaths among Christians in the UK today. They are also major contributors to diabetes, accidents (especially injuries from falls) and spine and joint problems. When we consider individual diseases, as above, we need to remember that some risk factors contribute to a whole variety of different diseases.

Smoking kills 100,000 people a year in the UK mainly through coronary heart disease, strokes, lung disease and various forms of cancer. [16] Alcohol-related liver disease kills about 6,000 people a year but the total number of alcohol-related deaths is around 24,000 if we add in alcohol-related deaths from accidents, violence, suicide, hypertension, stroke, coronary heart disease and cancers of the breast and gastrointestinal tract. [17]

Bill started smoking 20 cigarettes a day in his late teens and later increased it to 40. He had noticed that his exercise tolerance was decreasing but was finally brought to his senses at the age of 46 when he woke up in the early hours of the morning with crushing pain in his chest. His wife called the ambulance and he was rushed to hospital where an ECG and blood tests showed changes consistent with a small heart attack. He made a good recovery but realised that the outcome could well have been different and that his decision to smoke could have left his wife a widow and his children without a father. Giving up the cigarettes was not easy but his GP's sober warning about what might be around the corner if he continued was eventually incentive enough.

16. Smoking – The facts. *Patient.co.uk www.patient.co.uk/health/smoking-the-facts*
17. Alcohol 'could kill 210,000 in next 20 years'. *NHS Choices*, 20 February 2012 *bit.ly/1t50eHA*

It is estimated that there are around 35,000 obesity-related deaths in England each year. [18] This accounts for one in every 16 deaths. Obesity is a risk factor for high blood pressure (hypertension), heart disease, infertility, many types of cancer, stroke, type 2 diabetes, asthma, osteoarthritis, back pain, depression, liver and kidney disease, and sleep apnoea.

Body mass index (BMI) can be easily worked out from height and weight using an online calculator – just google 'BMI'! The normal range is 18.5–25 with 25–30 being overweight and over 30 being obese. For example, a 183cm (six foot) tall, 35 year old man weighing 80kg (12.5 stone) would have a BMI of 24, just at the upper range of normal.

Weight is determined by our calorie balance – calories eaten verses calories burned – but it is much easier to cut 500 calories from our daily diet than to burn an extra 500 calories every day. Two studies may explain why many people who begin exercise programmes often lose little to no weight in the long run. The first, published in the scientific journal *PLoS One*, compared the daily energy expenditures of Westerners and the Hadza, a population of hunter-gatherers living in northern Tanzania. [19] Amazingly it found no difference. The second study, in *Obesity Reviews*, found that when people exercise but keep their energy intake constant, their resting metabolic rate actually goes down. [20] The body resists weight loss by changing its 'idle speed'. In fact this is true of dieting alone too! These studies suggest two things: exercise programmes may not lead to as much calorie burn as we might think, and many people start eating more when they exercise, and may eat too much. [21]

18. Complications of obesity. NHS Choices *bit.ly/1uGi6qE*
19. Pontzer H et al. Hunter-gatherer energetics and human obesity. *PLoS ONE* 2012;7(7) *bit.ly/1oUzt1k*
20. Schwartz A and Doucet É. Relative changes in resting energy expenditure during weight loss: a systematic review. Obesity Reviews 2010;11 pp. 531–437
21. Is dieting or exercise better for losing weight? *Tufts Now*, January 31 2013 *bit.ly/1w2bzF4*

Geoff had represented his school in cross-country when he was 16 and later ran for the local harriers when he was at university. But marriage, children and a sedentary job changed all that and his body shape began to change. When his wife and teenage children teased him about getting fat he said he could still easily run around the block. When they fell about laughing he found some trainers and went for a two mile run. Finding himself waddling and completely out of breath after a mile he decided something had to be done. He reduced his diet and revised his work travelling schedule so that he was forced to walk at least two miles a day. Over the next few years he lost the extra ten kilograms he had put on and even ran a couple of half marathons. Now he feels much better, seems to keep illness more regularly at bay and is grateful for his family's rebuke. He looks at friends carrying 20kg more and realises how easily he could have followed them.

Although diet may be more important than exercise for weight loss, as these two studies show, exercise does contribute to weight loss and there are also many other benefits of exercise: less stress and anxiety, improved mood and less risk of cardiovascular disease, diabetes and some cancers. In 2012, a study in *The Lancet*, a leading medical journal, suggested that, worldwide, inactivity is killing as many people as smoking. [22] That equates to about one in ten deaths from diseases such as heart disease, diabetes and breast and colon cancer. It is recommended that adults do 150 minutes of moderate exercise, such as brisk walking, cycling or gardening, each week. It also found that people in higher-income countries were the least active, with those in the UK among the worst, as nearly two thirds of adults were judged not to be doing enough.

These are the medical facts, but how does the Bible help us think and act with regard to personal health?

---

22.   Inactivity 'killing as many as smoking'. *BBC News*, 18 July 2012 bbc.in/1nOYfRM

Biblical basics

We need to acknowledge first of all that we are mortal. We're all going to die, almost certainly of a disease or an accident – unless Jesus returns first! The apostle Paul reminds us that 'outwardly we are wasting away' and are clothed with an 'earthly tent' in which 'we groan and are burdened' (2 Corinthians 4:16–5:4). So we shouldn't be surprised when we or our loved ones eventually develop some serious illness. It is part of living in a fallen world. Rather we should expect it. It's part of the human journey. It is amazing how many people are genuinely shocked to find they have developed a serious illness, as though it was something they thought was never going to happen to them, or at least 'not yet'.

Medicine is a great gift and has made great advances, but all medicine is limited. All it really can offer is a few more years of better quality. It can delay death by treating some diseases and relieving others, but it cannot make us immortal.

Now there is another important biblical principle: We need also to remember that our bodies are gifts from God and temples of the Holy Spirit (1 Corinthians 6:19). This should lead us to treat them with respect, look after them carefully and use them in ways that are 'holy and honourable' (1 Thessalonians 4:4). In so doing, we may well also be lessening our chances of getting certain diseases.

Alcohol and drugs in the Bible

There are many warnings in Scripture about not abusing our bodies. The Bible contains no references to mind-altering substances which are now classified as harmful and illegal drugs, and the authors had no knowledge of tobacco. However the Bible does have a huge amount to say about alcohol – and the principles can be applied in these other areas too.

In the Old Testament we have salutary tales about Noah and Lot getting drunk and doing things they would later regret (Genesis 9:20–27, 19:30–38). If we drink too much alcohol we lose control of our judgment. Later there is the incident of the man who forfeits his life for being 'a profligate and a drunkard' (Deuteronomy 21:18–21). The Wisdom literature features vivid descriptions of the clinical effects of alcohol with warnings about its misuse. Proverbs 23:29–33 gives a stunningly accurate description of the clinical features of alcohol intoxication, including red eyes, injury with bruising, hallucinations, memory loss and addiction. Psalm 104:15 says that wine 'gladdens human hearts', a reminder that alcohol exaggerates our feelings – it does indeed gladden the heart of a cheerful person but also aggravates the depression of a sad one!

> Moyna did not consider herself to be a heavy drinker but regularly enjoyed a glass or two of wine a night and not infrequently was hung over on Sunday mornings after a Saturday night out. One night she took a corner too fast and rolled the car with three friends on board. The car was a write off but thankfully only one of her friends suffered minor injuries. However the police were called and she ended up being confirmed over the limit and losing her driving licence for a year. Shortly afterwards a routine visit to her GP and subsequent tests revealed abnormal liver function. Moyna tried to regulate her alcohol intake but realised that she was unable to and eventually decided to give up drinking altogether. Although he did not have a drinking problem himself, her husband decided also to abstain from all alcohol so as to minimise any temptation for her.

We see similar warnings in the New Testament. The apostle Paul exhorts the Ephesians, 'Do not get drunk on wine, which leads to debauchery. Instead, be filled with the Spirit' (Ephesians 5:18). Peter similarly lists 'drunkenness, orgies, carousing' among the things 'pagans choose to do' (1 Peter 4:3). Then there is the sober warning that along with other groups, 'drunkards' will not 'inherit the kingdom of God' (1 Corinthians 6:10).

And yet the Bible does not prohibit alcohol altogether. In fact the Bible also sees wine as a gift that is used in honour of God in Jewish festivals and as a symbol of the coming kingdom. Jesus himself was even accused of being a 'winebibber' (Matthew 11:19, KJV) or drunkard. Jesus' first miracle involved turning water into (rather a lot of) wine at Cana (John 2:1–11). Other passages in the Gospels record Jesus drinking with the socially undesirable, but as he never sinned, we know he was not a 'drunkard' like some of them were (Matthew 11:18–19; Luke 5:29–30, 7:33–34). Yet neither was the Son of God a teetotaller. At the Last Supper, Jesus took a cup of wine and gave it a new covenantal meaning as a symbol of his redeeming blood. Whether the Communion wine is alcoholic or non-alcoholic, almost all Christians celebrate that redemption regularly (Matthew 26:27–29; Mark 14:23–25; Luke 22:17–20; 1 Corinthians 11:23–34). Paul advised Timothy to 'Stop drinking only water, and use a little wine because of your stomach and your frequent illnesses' (1 Timothy 5:23). Notice, though, he says 'a little wine'! Admittedly, this was at a time when water for drinking was often harmfully laden with infective agents, and alcoholic drinks were nowhere near as strong as they are today.

So it is not wrong for Christians to drink alcohol, but it is always wrong to become drunk, or to drink to the point where we lose control of our faculties or start to damage our health. Some Christians may choose not to drink at all, perhaps because of a past alcohol problem or to avoid being a stumbling-block to others: 'Be careful, however, that the exercise of your freedom does not become a stumbling-block to the weak' (1 Corinthians 8:1–13).

What about smoking? Tobacco was unknown in biblical times, but while alcohol can be consumed so moderately that it is not harmful (and may even be beneficial), we now know beyond a shadow of a doubt that every cigarette does damage. Before this was known, it was regarded as almost normal in some quarters for Christians, including some famous Christian leaders, to smoke. But in view of what we now know, it is hard to see how this activity can be considered consistent with good stewardship of one's body.

However, we need to be careful not to judge those who have not yet been able to stop. Nicotine is powerfully addictive and those who fall under its spell, and that of other drugs, may well need prayer, support and professional help in order to break free.

Overeating in the Bible

Obesity is perhaps much more of a challenge to us than it was to those in biblical times. With changes in work and lifestyle, people exercise less, and with national changes in the sort of food we eat, we tend to consume more calories than we burn off. The Bible was written in times of hard physical work, to people who ate a 'Mediterranean diet'.[23] However there were some striking examples of people who were very overweight and whose weight may have contributed to their deaths. Eli the priest died when, hearing the news of his sons' deaths at war, he fell backwards and broke his neck 'for he was an old man, and he was heavy' (1 Samuel 4:18).

Eglon, king of Moab, died from a penetrating injury after being stabbed by Ehud the Israelite judge. We are told he was 'a very fat man' and we are given a very graphic description of his death: 'Ehud reached with his left hand, drew the sword from his right thigh and plunged it into the king's belly. Even the handle sank in after the blade, and his bowels discharged. Ehud did not pull the sword out, and the fat closed in over it' (Judges 3:17–22). Eglon's gross obesity and slow manoeuvrability might conceivably have made him an easier military target.

But it can be dangerous to draw Christian principles purely from Bible narrative, interesting those these cases are. We need to look at the Bible's more general teaching. The book of Proverbs gives wise advice to those given to gluttony (Proverbs 23:1–3, 20–21): 'Do not join those who drink too much wine or gorge themselves on meat, for drunkards and gluttons become poor, and drowsiness clothes them in rags.' It also warns those with a sweet tooth to 'eat just enough'

---

23. The principal aspects of a Mediterranean diet include proportionally high consumption of olive oil, legumes, unrefined cereals, fruits, and vegetables, moderate to high consumption of fish, moderate consumption of dairy products (mostly as cheese and yogurt), moderate wine consumption, and low consumption of meat and meat products.

(Proverbs 25:16) and states that 'a companion of gluttons disgraces his father' (Proverbs 28:7).

The apostle Paul remarks on the propensity of the inhabitants of Crete to be 'liars, evil brutes, lazy gluttons' and exhorts Titus to rebuke them and urge them to 'be sound in the faith' (Titus 1:12, 13). He similarly warns the Philippians: 'Many live as enemies of the cross of Christ. Their destiny is destruction, their god is their stomach, and their glory is in their shame' (Philippians 3:18–19).

So far we have focused largely on drugs and diet. But we need to remember that sexual health and mental health are also important contributors to wellbeing. They can have profound effects on eating and drinking behaviour. The present explosion in the number of cases of sexually transmitted infections is a graphic warning of the consequences of unhealthy lifestyle choices. How many people drink too much or eat too much in order to comfort themselves in anxiety, in depression or over some sexual sin?

Rest and devotional times

Christians, because of a strong desire to serve, may also neglect their need for proper rest and make themselves more vulnerable to illness through overwork or lack of sleep. Jesus was not legalistic about the Sabbath but rather recognised its true purpose. He realised that it was important to withdraw and rest, even in the face of pressing need. Burnout can be a major problem for Christians because we are motivated by a strong sense of responsibility and are aware of the vast amount of unmet need. But we also need to schedule time for relaxation and recuperation. How we spend it will depend on our own personality and makeup. We may be alone or with others, doing a vigorous activity or a sedentary one – the important thing is that we take time out altogether from work and ministry at regular intervals.

The story is told of two men who chopped wood. One stopped for regular rests every hour while the other just kept chopping all day long. At the end of the day the one who rested had a far larger pile of chopped wood. The other was surprised until he learned that while resting, the other had also been sharpening his axe. Recognising the need for rest is like sharpening the axe.

Jesus said, 'Take my yoke upon you and learn from me, for I am gentle and humble in heart, and you will find rest for your souls. For my yoke is easy and my burden is light' (Matthew 11:29–30). Jesus also guarded his devotional life. He spent time in prayer, especially during periods of intense activity. He prayed regularly and especially before each important decision. And he withdrew from his ministry to pray after periods of exhausting ministry. In Luke 5:15–16 we find a good prescription for busy Christians in the example of Jesus: '...crowds of people came to hear him and to be healed of their sicknesses. But Jesus often withdrew to lonely places and prayed'. The more he worked the more he prayed. He was 'too busy not to pray'. Perhaps God creates the delays and stoppages in our busy lives; the red lights, and traffic jams, the queues and holdups so that we might have the opportunity to pray more.

Similarly Jesus was immersed in the word of God – so much so that when the devil challenged him in the wilderness he could answer with three quotes from the book of Deuteronomy; a book that many of us could not easily find, let alone quote from. Do we regularly feed on God's word? Do we make it one of our first priorities? Jesus did.

Keeping it all in perspective

The main emphasis of this chapter has been on the importance of taking a healthy interest in our physical health. But there is an opposite danger – that of being health and fitness obsessed. For some, including Christians, maintaining health and fitness can become a god in itself and lead to an over-occupation with one's body and longevity that is spiritually very unhealthy. We need therefore to keep health in an eternal perspective. The Bible says that all people 'are destined to die once and after that to face judgment' (Hebrews 9:27) and then to end up in one of two destinations for all eternity (Revelation 20:11–15). That is something that wonderfully focuses the mind about priorities on earth!

So let's not be scared of cancer. If it happens, it happens. Instead let's grasp the fact that there is actually something far worse than cancer. As Jesus said, 'I will show you whom you should fear: fear him who, after your body has been killed, has authority to throw you into hell. Yes, I tell you, fear him' (Luke 12:5).

Salvation – knowing, enjoying and glorifying God in his worldwide family forever – is infinitely more important than good health in this life and we should always comfort ourselves with this thought. The wonderful truth is that 'Christ was sacrificed once to take away the sins of many' and that 'he will appear a second time, not to bear sin, but to bring salvation to those who are waiting for him' (Hebrews 9:28). Our destiny is not to live on in these bodies we have now, but to receive bodies like that of Jesus after the resurrection in order to live in a 'New Jerusalem' where there will be 'no more death or mourning or crying or pain' (Philippians 3:21; Revelation 21:1–4). This life is only a shadow of what is to come, and the life that follows is infinitely more important. Therefore, we must avoid giving personal health too high a place in our lives. Health is a blessing but it is possible to make an idol of health and to put it before God himself.

There is no doubt that physical exercise is good for us. The apostle Paul uses athletes as examples of people who demonstrate self-discipline. But he does it primarily to emphasise the importance of spiritual fitness:

> *Do you not know that in a race all the runners compete,*
> *but only one receives the prize? So run that you may obtain it.*
> *Every athlete exercises self-control in all things. They do it to*
> *receive a perishable wreath, but we an imperishable.*
> (1 Corinthians 9:24–25)

In counselling his protégé Timothy, Paul exhorts him: 'train yourself to be godly. For physical training is of some value, but godliness has value for all things, holding promise for both the present life and the life to come' (1 Timothy 4:7–8). Physical training is of 'some value', but what good is a sleek and trim body with rippling biceps and tight abs if the person who owns it is ultimately destined for hell? As Jesus warned, 'What good is it for someone to gain the whole world, and yet lose or forfeit their very self?' (Luke 9:25).

Why guard our health?

There are many good reasons to care for our personal health. It may mean that we live longer in better health and can therefore be more help to and less dependent on our relatives, loved ones and members of the community. How much welfare dependency, early bereavement or time lost from work, is the result of poor lifestyle choices? How many families have been deprived of a bread-winner, parent, child or spouse when it could have been avoided? How much of the load the health service strains under is due to poor lifestyle choices? It may well mean that our own earthly lives involve less physical suffering through being able to avoid illness for longer and living a greater proportion of our lives disease free.

Perhaps above all, taking care of our bodies is a strong witness that we consider them to be gifts of a good creator that should be treasured, and that we look forward to the resurrection of our bodies on the day of judgment. When the apostle Peter spoke of the end times and the judgment, he asked his readers: 'Since everything will be destroyed in this way, what kind of people ought you to be?' He went on to answer his own question:

> You ought to live holy and godly lives as you look forward to the day of God and speed its coming... So then, dear friends, since you are looking forward to this, make every effort to be found spotless, blameless and at peace with him.
> (2 Peter 3:11–12, 14)

Caring for our bodies is surely part of living 'holy and godly lives' and making 'every effort to be found spotless'. For 'in keeping with his promise we are looking forward to a new heaven and a new earth, where righteousness dwells' (2 Peter 3:10–14).

FURTHER READING

- Bunn A, Randall D. Health benefits of Christian faith. *CMF Files* 44, 2011 *bit.ly/1oyHFnI*
- Cook C. Problem drinking: The bigger picture. *Triple Helix* 2005; Summer pp. 8–9 *bit.ly/ZrOqUw*
- Daly M. Facing the obesity epidemic. *Triple Helix* 2004; Autumn pp. 10–11 *bit.ly/1oyHDfC*
- Dixon P. The truth about drugs. *Nucleus* 1999; Autumn pp. 26–32. *bit.ly/ZrOp2P*
- Lambley R. Ashes to ashes: The tobacco industry. *Nucleus* 2001; pp. 5–7 *bit.ly/1oyHFnG*
- Latham J. Addiction: A view from the front line. *Nucleus* 2003; Autumn pp. 14–21 *bit.ly/1oyHFnH*
- Leach M, Leach S. Addiction: Helping others and ourselves. *Nucleus* 2000; Winter pp. 23–29 *bit.ly/ZrOp2N*
- Roach J. Banning smoking: A welcome proposal. *Triple Helix* 2005; Winter pp. 3 *bit.ly/ZrOp2O*
- Short D. Beating burnout. *Triple Helix* 2001; Summer pp. 10–11 *bit.ly/1oyHDfD*
- Vere D. Dependence and addiction. *CMF Files* 8, 1999 *bit.ly/1oyHDfE*
- Watts D. Drugs and alcohol: Why should we care? *Triple Helix* 2010; Easter pp. 10–11 *bit.ly/1oyHDfB*

CHAPTER 5

MENTAL HEALTH:
AM I SUPPOSED TO FEEL LIKE THIS?

Do not be anxious about anything, but in every situation,
by prayer and petition, with thanksgiving, present your
requests to God. And the peace of God, which transcends all
understanding, will guard your hearts and your minds in Christ
Jesus. Finally, brothers and sisters, whatever is true, whatever
is noble, whatever is right, whatever is pure, whatever is lovely,
whatever is admirable – if anything is excellent or praiseworthy
– think about such things. Whatever you have learned or
received or heard from me, or seen in me – put it into
practice. And the God of peace will be with you.
(Philippians 4:6–9)

M ental illness is incredibly common. About one in four people will experience some kind of mental health problem in the course of a year. [1] Mixed anxiety and depression is the most common mental disorder in Britain, with around 9% of people meeting criteria for diagnosis. [2] All ages are affected too – about 10% of children have a mental health problem [3] at any one time and depression affects one in five older people. [4]

Psychiatry is the medical specialty that deals specifically with disorders of the mind. We are much better now than in previous centuries at recognising and treating mental illness. The reliability

---

1.   Mental health statistics: UK and worldwide. Mental Health Foundation *bit.ly/1rSzpBJ*
2.   Adult psychiatric morbidity report. The Office for National Statistics, 2007 *bit.ly/1qD7310*
3.   Mental health statistics: Children & young people. Mental Health Foundation *bit.ly/1wv3dcN*
4.   Mental health statistics: Older people *bit.ly/1sVsV7t*

of some psychiatric diagnoses has been shown to exceed that, say, of a speciality with 'hard' facts such as radiology and there have been huge advances in the treatments available for many psychiatric conditions. People, who in past centuries would have been hospitalised for long periods or placed in 'lunatic asylums', can now be treated effectively using medication or the various 'talking therapies' in the community. As a result, many people with very serious mental illnesses are now able to function well in families, communities and the workplace. The treatment of schizophrenia, for example, was revolutionised by medications developed during the twentieth century. Others with less serious problems are able to live normal lives and lots of people get better. Some mental disorders are still very difficult to treat, but new inroads are being made all the time.

As with physical disorders, the various mental disorders have been laboriously classified after careful study and the various categories of illness are regularly reviewed and refined as specialist knowledge grows and improves. There are two main classifications for mental illnesses: the UK uses the World Health Organisation's *International Classification of Diseases* (ICD); in the USA the American Psychiatric Association's *Diagnostic and Statistical Manual of Mental Disorders* (DSM) is used. Both of these are regularly updated as new knowledge comes to light and various disorders are added, removed or reclassified. There are literally hundreds of different mental disorders, although as for physical diseases, some are common household names and some are exceedingly rare and known only to sufferers and specialists. To give an idea of this breadth, the list below shows the ten main categories within the ICD-10, along with one or two better-known examples of each. Many of these are well known but the list also contains some technical terms that may not be familiar to the general reader. The details are not important. The intention is simply to convey the broad range of mental illnesses that are recognised.

- Organic, including symptomatic, mental disorders
  (eg Alzheimer's dementia)

- Mental and behavioural disorders due to psychoactive substance use (eg alcohol dependency)
- Schizophrenia and delusional disorders (eg paranoid schizophrenia)
- Mood (affective) disorders (eg depression and bipolar affective disorder)
- Neurotic, stress-related and somatoform disorders (eg agoraphobia and post-traumatic stress disorder)
- Behavioural syndromes associated with physiological disturbances and physical factors (eg anorexia nervosa and bulimia)
- Disorders of adult personality and behaviour (eg borderline personality disorder and pathological gambling)
- Learning disability
- Disorders of psychological development (eg autism and Asperger syndrome)
- Behavioural and emotional disorders with onset usually occurring in childhood and adolescence (eg attention deficit hyperactivity disorder (ADHD) and separation anxiety)
- Unspecified mental disorder

To qualify as a mental disorder a condition must fulfil a number of carefully defined diagnostic criteria, which is why both diagnosis and treatment of mental illnesses are things only trained specialists are really qualified to do. Being anxious or feeling low are not the same as having an anxiety disorder or being diagnosed with clinical depression but this is often poorly understood by the public and also by many pastors and church members. But just as one would not try to treat lung cancer without specialist help, neither should one take on a real mental illness.

There is thankfully much less stigma attached to mental disorders nowadays, and much better understanding, which means that those who suffer from them are treated with far more compassion and better care than was the case in the past. But there is still much progress to be made. Sadly there is still a level of stigma within the church. For example, how many people do you know who are happy to admit that they are taking antidepressants as opposed to antibiotics?

Some people believe in ignorance that Christians should be somehow immune to these kinds of problems when in fact they are part and parcel of life.

> Ben was struggling at school and had very few friends.
> He was referred by his teacher to a community paediatrician who diagnosed him as being on the autism spectrum.
> His parents were deeply concerned at the diagnosis but also somewhat relieved that his behaviour now had an explanation.
> However, friends at church unhelpfully blamed their parenting skills. Through a local support group for affected families they were put in touch with a coach who helped them develop skills to handle Ben's behaviour more effectively. They came to see that they were not bad parents but rather ordinary parents struggling with a challenging child. Through their experiences they were able to help their church friends gain a deeper understanding about mental health issues in children and be more understanding and supportive.

What causes mental illness?

Genes, physical and social environment and lifestyle choices all play a part in our mental health. Several schools of thought have developed which attempt to explain why a particular person has developed a particular disorder. We can illustrate these various approaches by considering depression. What causes it?

Behavioural models of depression might see it as learning a pattern of helplessness. If you cannot get away from pain you soon despair and give up trying. And consequentially, a distorted view of the world might lead to habitual negative thoughts and interpretations of events. This is called a *cognitive*–behavioural model.

Sociological models of depression focus on social isolation or too many major life events occurring over a short period of time. It is known, for example, that divorce, followed by a house move and subsequent unemployment is a powerful predisposing cocktail.

Existential models might attribute depression to a loss of meaning and purpose or a failure to find it. Victor Frankl (1905–1997), a psychiatrist associated with this school of thought, was a Jewish concentration camp survivor who noted that those who came through Auschwitz less traumatised psychologically were those who had a sense of meaning to their lives.

Psychoanalytical models are classically associated with Sigmund Freud. This school might see the causes of depresion in aggression turned inwards, early loss of a mother ('breaking the bonds of love') or loss of self-esteem as a result of a dysfunctional family.

Finally, *biological* models attribute depression to biochemical change in the brain, specifically impairment of monoamine function and disruption of nerve pathways, affecting chemicals like serotonin and noradrenalin (norepinephrine).

So, what are we to make of all these models? Can they all be true? Each of them has some scientific evidence which supports it. Negative thoughts, social isolation, loss of purpose, disturbed family relationships and biochemical changes may all play a part to some extent in any given case of depression. This perhaps explains in part why depression has been shown to respond to a variety of different treatments including medication, regular exercise, electroconvulsive (ECT) therapy and talking therapies like cognitive behavioural therapy (CBT). These are all treatments with a proven track record. Being in a supportive community and being involved in work or activities that give one meaning and purpose are of course also very important. But it is both dangerous and simplistic for Christians to tell others that prayer and fellowship are all they need and that they shouldn't be taking antidepressants or having CBT. Can we imagine telling someone with diabetes that he should just pray rather than taking exercise, watching his diet and taking insulin? Worryingly, these attitudes are still found in some churches.

Secular models of mental illness all provide some help to us and we need to recognise that, while none of them is complete, each has at least an element of truth that resonates to some extent with biblical principles. Behavioural approaches emphasise the importance of developing good habits. Sociological models underline the value of growing up with a strong support network of family and friends. Existential models show the value of having a reason to live and psychological models demonstrate how crucial the influences in our formative years are. Biological models are a reminder that our brains function by way of electrical signals mediated by chemical substances and that these pathways can become disturbed.

Mind and body

The Japanese athletic equipment company ASICS derives its name from the acronym for the Latin phrase *anima sana in corpore sano* which translates as 'a sound mind in a sound body'. The close connection between the mind and the body has long been recognised. The ancient Greek philosopher Plato (c.428–c.347 BC) said in his work *Charmides*, 'For this… is the great error of our day in the treatment of the human body, that physicians separate the soul from the body.' Philosophers and scientists right down to the present day debate how exactly the two entities of mind and body interact with each other, but there is no doubt that our bodily make up influences our thoughts and feelings and that our thoughts and feelings have an impact on the functioning of our bodies.

As we saw in chapter one, the Bible teaches that we are embodied souls or ensouled bodies, a complex unity of spirit, soul and body (1 Thessalonians 5:23). The very same verse tells us that God intends to sanctify us (make us holy) 'through and through' and that our 'whole spirit, soul and body' be kept blameless. In order to be fully effective, healthcare must also be 'wholistic'. It must address people's needs, understanding that they are whole persons, and not *just* bodies or *just* souls.

Thoughts, feelings and actions

As whole persons, our thoughts and feelings matter to God, just as our bodily actions do. The Bible speaks a lot about all three. When we look at worldviews other than Christianity they tend to fall into one of three groups. First are those that are rooted in thinking: Master this idea, understand this problem, analyse this situation. Foundational to Buddhism, for example, is grasping the four noble truths. Next are those, like New Age Pantheism, which are rooted in feeling: Have this experience, know this feeling. Finally there are those which are rooted in action: Don't ask the big questions, the answers are irrelevant anyway, just get on with the practical realities. Postmodernism, and to some extent existentialism, reject the search for an overarching 'metanarrative' or big story behind reality.

Christianity is different. It is not primarily a set of ideas, experiences or instructions on how to live. Nor is its ultimate authority found in any of those three. Rather, the gospel is rooted in a relationship with the person of Jesus Christ, God the Son who took on human flesh and lived among us (John 1:14). Being called, by God's grace, to be 'imitators of Christ' (1 Corinthians 11:1, ESV), to take up our cross and follow him (Matthew 16:24) and to 'live as Jesus lived' (1 John 2:6) involves a personal commitment of our whole selves.

Here we need to return to the fundamental Christian worldview principles which we laid out in chapter one. In the beginning, God created human beings who were physically and mentally perfect (Genesis 1:31). Their thoughts, feelings and actions were all in harmony with God. But this did not mean that they were independent and without needs. Being made in God's image (Genesis 1:27) their spiritual needs were met through a loving 'face-to-face' relationship with God. Their social needs were met through relationships with others (Genesis 2:18). Their need for meaningful occupation and purpose was met through being made responsible for the earth (Genesis 1:28) and caring for the garden (Genesis 2:15). Human beings had control of their environment. There was harmony with nature, no illness or death (Genesis 1:29, 2:9, 19) and they were at peace with themselves: 'The man and woman were both naked and they felt no shame' (Genesis 2:25). There was no anxiety, no inner conflicts and no guilt.

Fallen creatures

Before the Fall, man and woman found perfect fulfilment in their relationship with God and with each other. Their need for love, purpose, security and significance were completely met and thus there was no predisposition to depression or anxiety. But as a result of the Fall, these previously perfect relationships were destroyed. There was separation from God (Genesis 3:8) and separation and exploitation between men and women (Genesis 3:12, 16). There was internal disintegration leading to fear, shame and anxiety. As a result human beings sought to hide from God, shrank into themselves and began hiding from each other and perhaps even themselves. Work became a frustrating burden and there was loss of control over the environment (Genesis 3:17, 19). Pain and death entered the world and the harmony with nature was lost (Genesis 3:16, 19). The account of the Fall shows us that the effects of sin permeate every area of life – genes, personalities, relationships, work, relationship with God and physical and mental health.

As we are all subject to the effects of the Fall, we are all similarly susceptible to mental illness simply by virtue of being fallen human beings. But our susceptibility will vary depending on our genetic makeup, personal experiences and lifestyle choices. In other words, nature and nurture (heredity and environment) play a part along with personal choice in affecting our mental health, just as they do our physical health. We now know that in many mental illnesses there are real biochemical changes in the brain. There is also the effect others' sin and folly has on us (eg child abuse, trauma). This interplay with 'the choices of others' is particularly prevalent in mental illness.

How Christian faith can help

While Christians are susceptible to mental disorders like anyone else, there is no doubt that being a member of a Christian church and having a Christian faith both offers protection against some kinds of mental illness and also helps recovery. This is equally true of some physical illnesses and has been attributed to the transformation of thinking and behaviour that accompanies Christian conversion and growth as a disciple of Jesus and being part of a loving community. Churches have a huge role to play in helping people with mental illnesses, whether they are believers or not. The importance of listening, acceptance, providing encouragement to seek proper treatment, care and support for carers and creating an environment free from stigma cannot be overemphasised.

Evidence from over 1,200 studies and 400 reviews has shown an association between faith and a number of positive health benefits, including protection from illness, coping with illness, and faster recovery from it. Of the studies reviewed in the definitive analysis by Koenig and Larson 81% showed benefit and only 4% harm. Their conclusions about mental health are striking:

> In the majority of studies, religious involvement is correlated with wellbeing, happiness and life satisfaction; hope and optimism; purpose and meaning in life; higher self-esteem; better adaptation to bereavement; greater social support and less loneliness; lower rates of depression and faster recovery from depression; lower rates of suicide and fewer positive attitudes towards suicide; less anxiety; less psychosis and fewer psychotic tendencies; lower rates of alcohol and drug abuse; less delinquency and criminal activity; greater marital stability and satisfaction. [5]

Emeritus Professor and former President of the Royal College of Psychiatrists Andrew Sims has lamented the lack of attention given to this strong evidence by secular doctors: 'for anything other than religion and spirituality, governments and health providers would be doing their utmost to promote it'. [6]

---

5. Koenig HG, McCullough ME, Larson DB. *Handbook of religion and health*. Oxford University Press, 2001
6. Sims A. *Is faith delusion? Why religion is good for your health*. Continuum, 2009

If we think about it, it is perhaps not surprising that Christian faith has a positive impact on mental health. As Christians we have been born again of the Spirit (John 3:16) and given new natures as a result of Jesus' death and resurrection (2 Corinthians 5:17). We have come to know that God, who created the universe, loves us and that nothing can separate us from his love (Romans 8:28–39). We have a glorious future to look forward to beyond the grave (1 Corinthians 2:9) and have joined a community of like-minded people who are equipped by God to love and support us (Ephesians 4:11–16). Christian discipleship involves a transformation of thoughts and actions, made possible by God's mighty resurrection power. Therefore one would expect it also to have an influence on our moods and feelings, and it most certainly does.

Let's turn to examine in more depth what the Scriptures teach us about safeguarding and managing mental health. As we will see, there is not much about the diagnosis and treatment of specific mental disorders but there is a huge deal about handling our thoughts and feelings and submitting our whole selves – body, soul and spirit – to the Lordship of Christ.

Mental illness in the Bible

It is sometimes incorrectly assumed that the Bible makes no reference to mental illness as an entity in itself, but this is simply not true. The Bible teaches that on occasions diseases may arise because of demonic influence, and that this may sometimes be the case with mental illness as with physical illness. Saul's depression in 1 Samuel 16:14–23 is a good example. We are told that Saul was tormented by an evil spirit 'from the Lord' reminding us that God is sovereign over all the powers of evil. However, most mentions of mental illness in the Bible make no reference to demons at all.

The concept of the 'madman' was very familiar to the biblical writers. David feigned insanity while in the presence of the Philistine king by 'making marks on the doors of the gate and letting saliva run down his beard' in order to protect himself (1 Samuel 21:12–14).

The prophet Hosea says that in an evil age 'the prophet is considered a fool, the inspired person a maniac' (Hosea 9:7). In keeping with this, Jehu's servants called the prophet who anointed him a 'maniac' (2 Kings 9:11–12) and the false prophet Shemaiah referred to Jeremiah in the same way (Jeremiah 29:24–28). Jesus' family at one stage thought he was 'out of his mind' (Mark 3:21) and Festus said that Paul's great learning was driving him insane (Acts 26:24).

But perhaps the best description of a real (but extremely rare) mental illness in Scripture is that of Nebuchadnezzar's insanity in Daniel 4. It was characterised by rapid onset (v33), with spontaneous remission after an unspecified interval (v34). His behaviour (eating grass and allowing his hair and nails to grow long) is suggestive of lycanthropy; a delusion in which the patient believes himself to be an animal. This may be caused by a variety of psychiatric conditions including a depressive illness, schizophrenia, mania, an organic brain syndrome (like dementia) or a hysterical (dissociative) state.

Despite Daniel's warning to 'renounce [his] sins by doing what is right, and [his] wickedness by being kind to the oppressed' (v27), the proud leader of Babylon refused to humble himself and repent – his illness in this case was actually a fulfilment of prophecy:

> You will be driven away from people and will live with the wild animals; you will eat grass like cattle and be drenched with the dew of heaven. Seven times will pass by for you until you acknowledge that the Most High is sovereign over the kingdoms of men and gives them to anyone he wishes.
> (Daniel 4:24–25)

The incident is a sober warning about human pride… but also a testimony to divine mercy and sovereignty. Nebuchadnezzar's mental illness was related specifically to his personal sin, but this is very unusual. As we will see, many Christians, including some outstanding leaders, have suffered and still suffer today from disabling mental illnesses. We are therefore much better thinking of mental illness in the same way as physical illness – something we are all susceptible to.

Believers struggle too

The fact that God is sovereign even over mental illness is incredibly important to grasp as many Christians suffer from mental illnesses at some time in their lives. Hymn writer William Cowper (1731–1800) and preacher Charles Spurgeon (1834–1892) are two examples of very prominent and highly productive British Christians used mightily by God, yet who struggled throughout their lives with depression.

When Gordon began hearing voices, his Christian friends wondered if he might be demon-possessed and tried to pray for him. But when he told them that he had been chosen by God to bring peace to the world and started acting very strangely they became more concerned. Eventually when he tried climbing out the window at a prayer meeting to get away from the devil they sought professional help. Gordon was sectioned and admitted to a secure psychiatric ward where he was diagnosed with a psychotic disorder and started on medication which eventually controlled the symptoms. He now functions reasonably well in his community and holds down a part-time job but is kept under regular review. Furthermore his friends and family know the danger signs that should lead them to seek help earlier in the event of a relapse.

Spurgeon produced more publications throughout his life than any Christian writer in world history and Cowper penned some of our most famous hymns including 'There is a fountain filled with blood' and 'God moves in a mysterious way'. God used their illnesses to enhance their creativity and insight. Cowper's story is a poignant reminder that God's power is made perfect in weakness and that mental illness is not a sign of him abandoning us (2 Corinthians 12:9). Cowper faced repeated periods of severe depression until his death in the year 1800 and was never fully free of it. He was often suicidal and on occasions attempted unsuccessfully to take his own life. But he was helped to cope through the friendship of his pastor, former slave trader John Newton (1725–1807), who penned 'Amazing Grace', one of the world's most famous hymns. With practical love and constant companionship, Newton walked with Cowper through the dark times and gave him the support that made his illness bearable.

Just as many Christians will suffer from physical illness for which there is no full cure but only periodic relief, many also will suffer from mental illness from which they may never be fully free. This is a key area where we need to bear one another's burdens. Many other Christians, although not suffering from true mental illness, will know times of high anxiety or deep despondency. It is therefore an encouragement to know that the apostle Paul says that he and his companions were 'under great pressure, far beyond our ability to endure, so that we despaired even of life' and were later 'harassed at every turn – conflicts on the outside, fears within' (2 Corinthians 1:8, 7:5). It seems Paul, even given his wonderful experiences of God, at times also felt very low indeed.

Daniel had a 'glass half empty' attitude to life, meaning that he was frequently down and despondent and regularly beat himself up for what he perceived to be poor performance in his work. During low periods he tended to resort to comfort eating and over a few years had put on a lot of weight which he found very difficult to shake off. This made him feel even worse. He worried that his inability to exercise better self-control was evidence of not being a Christian at all and he suffered feelings of doubt and despair and even contemplated taking his own life. A Christian friend encouraged him to read some books on Christian discipleship and holiness and through these he gained a better understanding of who he was as a new creature in Christ and what Christ's death and resurrection had achieved for him. Gradually he noticed his dark periods begin to lift and he learnt better to take control of his negative thoughts and replace them uplifting biblical truths. He still, more often than not, sees the glass as half empty but is able now to be much more objective about his temperament and personality and handle his thoughts more effectively.

Some Christians fall prone to an enslaving perfectionism in which they flagellate themselves for experiencing feelings that are not only a normal part of being human, but also part of the normal Christian life. It is not helpful either to feel anxious that we are anxious or despondent that we feel down, or even worse, to feel we have somehow let God down because of the way we feel. It is true that 'perfect love drives out fear' (1 John 4:18) but the truth is that our own love in this life will never be perfect. As the apostle John says, 'This is love: not that we loved God, *but that he loved us* and sent his Son as an atoning sacrifice for our sins' (1 John 4:10, emphasis added). In other words, such inward trials are intended to drive us to the foot of the cross to find help in our time of need (1 Corinthians 10:13; Hebrews 4:16).

The greatest comfort of all is for us to know that Jesus was made like us 'in every way', has 'himself suffered' (Hebrews 2:17–18) and is able to 'sympathise with our weaknesses' because he has been 'tempted in every way, just as we are' (Hebrews 4:15). As he bore our sins on the cross, Jesus knew mental torment and physical sufferings beyond anything we will ever experience such that he cried 'My God, my God, why have you forsaken me?' (Mark 15:34). In one of Isaiah's servant songs, prophetic of Christ, the prophet says, 'I have laboured to no purpose; I have spent my strength in vain for nothing' (Isaiah 49:4). What an encouragement it is that Jesus actually was tempted to feel this way. Matthew Bridges' (1800–1894) and Godfrey Thring's (1823–1903) great hymn 'Crown him with many crowns' speaks of this King Jesus: '...Crown him the Son of Man who every grief has known, that wrings the human breast, and takes and bears them for his own that all in him may rest'. Paul recognised that God allowed the mental torment in his life and that of his companions so that 'we might not rely on ourselves but God, who raises the dead' (2 Corinthians 1:9).

The prophet Elijah's mental meltdown in 1 Kings 19 after his encounter with the prophets of Baal is often referred to as a post-mountain-top experience. He runs in fear from the treacherous Queen Jezebel, loses perspective and asks God to take his life. God's prescription instead is rest, food, drink, a reassurance of his love, a fresh filling of the Holy Spirit, reinforcements and a new job to do (1 Kings 19:1–21). These are wonderful practical provisions for all who have been wounded in the Lord's service.

In a deeply mysterious passage in Hebrews we learn that Jesus 'learned obedience from what he suffered, and once made perfect, he became the source of eternal salvation for all who obey him' (Hebrews 5:9). This is not to say that Jesus was ever disobedient. The key is to understand that the word translated 'perfect' (*teleios*) actually means 'mature'. It is the same word Jesus uses in the Sermon on the Mount when he says, 'Be perfect, therefore as your heavenly Father is perfect' (Matthew 5:48). Jesus' sufferings, including his mental sufferings, were the testing ground in which his obedience became full grown. In the same way our own trials help us to rely on God and bring us to spiritual maturity (1 Peter 1:6–7).

The on-going battle

The Christian life is a battle against those three formidable enemies: the world, the flesh and the devil. The key is to realise that Christians fight this battle from a position of great strength because of what Jesus' death and resurrection have achieved for us. Jesus now sits at God's right hand, 'far above all rule and authority, power and dominion' and God has 'placed all things under his feet' (Ephesians 1:20–22). But the wonderful reality is that God has also 'raised us up with Christ and seated us with him' (Ephesians 2:6).

The world is formidable. However, Jesus lives in us by his Spirit and has overcome it: 'I have told you these things, so that in me you may have peace. In this world you will have trouble. But take heart! I have overcome the world' (John 16:33). The flesh (our sinful nature) is challenging. But 'by the Spirit' we can 'put to death the misdeeds of the body' (Romans 8:13) because we have 'been buried with him in baptism' (Colossians 2:12). Those who belong to Jesus Christ have 'crucified the flesh with its passions and desires' (Galatians 5:24). The devil is powerful, but Jesus has 'disarmed the powers and authorities… triumphing over them by the cross' (Colossians 2:15). Satan has to ask permission to test Job or sift Peter (Job 1:8–12, 2:3–6; Luke 22:31–32). Even the devil himself is under the sovereign authority of God and can only do what God allows.

Grasping these key biblical truths will help us hugely in the fight of faith. But the Christian faith is not easy and so God gives us lots of help in his word specifically to help us in overcoming feelings of anxiety and despondency.

Renewing our minds

People who are struggling with mental illnesses like depression need to make use of the very best medicine has to offer. In fact a course of antidepressants or other treatment may well be required in order to give them the initial lift they need in order to adopt new patterns of thinking.

> Kevin had suffered a minor bout of depression at university after a painful breakup with his girlfriend and had temporarily needed medication. But when his brother was killed in a road accident in his late twenties he suffered a much more severe episode which required temporary hospitalisation. Medication helped, but as a Christian he felt that he should have got over his difficulties more easily and he felt guilty that he was not being a good witness. The comments of some Christian friends did not help and his pastor suggested that there was an unresolved 'sin issue' in his life. Kevin's GP referred him to a psychiatrist who introduced him to cognitive behavioural therapy (CBT) and he moved churches to be under faithful biblical teaching which helped him to deepen his faith. A combination of the medicine, CBT and some supportive friends eventually helped him through and he was able to reduce his medication although was not able to come off it fully.

Cognitive behavioural therapy (CBT) is based on the idea that our thoughts have a powerful influence on our feelings. CBT, given through a therapist or via self-help books, is aimed at helping people to reject unhelpful thought patterns and to think and act in ways that lead to freedom and flourishing. Many Christian psychiatrists have been involved in its development and its underlying principles are both biblically sound and evidence-based. Feelings are important but in our generation they have assumed a place they were never intended to have. This imbalance is summed up in a memorable quote from the Margaret Thatcher biopic *The Iron Lady* (2011):

> *Do you know, one of the greatest problems of our age is that we are governed by people who care more about feelings than they do about thoughts and ideas? Now, thoughts and ideas, that interests me... Watch your thoughts for they become words. Watch your words for they become actions. Watch your actions for they become... habits. Watch your habits, for they become your character. And watch your character, for it becomes your destiny! What we think, we become.*

This captures the importance of thoughts in the formation of actions, habits, character and ultimately destiny. Our feelings are also usually triggered by our thoughts. Therefore it can be helpful, in overcoming both anxiety and despondency and preventing them in future, to recognise the thoughts that have led to these feelings. This is why the Bible can help people of faith to think in constructive and more helpful ways. The devil's powerbase is wrong ideas. If he can tempt us to believe the wrong things, then he can leave us also feeling fearful and down and render us less effective in our Christian service. If he can tempt us to wallow in self-destructive feelings, then all the better.

Effective spiritual warfare involves gradually moving from false beliefs and unhelpful thoughts and instead laying hold of truth. This is of course easier said than done, and like any change we need to see this as a gradual process. 'The weapons we fight with are not the weapons of the world. On the contrary, they have divine power to demolish strongholds. We demolish arguments and every pretension that sets itself up against the knowledge of God, and we take captive every thought to make it obedient to Christ' (2 Corinthians 10:4–5).

Much of the armour of God involves a healthy examination of our thoughts. We are to take the belt of truth, shield of faith, the breastplate of righteousness, the readiness of the gospel of peace, the helmet of salvation, the sword of the Sprit, which is the word of God, and prayer (Ephesians 6:14–18). All of these involve taking things that are already true and actively making them our own: a Christian tempted to despair reminds herself of the truth that nothing (even these feelings) can separate her from the love of God (Romans 8:38–39); that though faithless she remains in Christ's grip because he is always faithful; that her salvation has been achieved through Christ's action and not her own.

In Colossians, Paul urges his readers to 'put to death' one set of actions, thoughts and desires and to 'clothe yourselves' with another befitting their new status as God's people (Colossians 3:5–14). In Galatians he calls them to 'live by the Spirit' and thereby to exhibit its fruit of 'love, joy, peace, forbearance, kindness, goodness, faithfulness, gentleness and self-control'. As a natural result they will not 'gratify the desires of the sinful nature' (Galatians 5:16–26).

The letter to the Philippians ends with the charge to think and act correctly with the promise that this is the way to peace:

> *Finally, brothers and sisters, whatever is true, whatever is noble, whatever is right, whatever is pure, whatever is lovely, whatever is admirable – if anything is excellent or praiseworthy – think about such things. Whatever you have learned or received or heard from me, or seen in me – put it into practice. And the God of peace will be with you.*
> (Philippians 4:8–9)

The Psalms practically illustrate this process of turning around fear, anxiety and despair into courage, hope and contentment. They show us spiritual discipline in action and together cover every possible state of mind that we might find ourselves in. The disciple finds himself drowning in problems, under attack, assailed from every direction and defeated, but reminds himself of God's liberating truth and faithful promises. But, by confronting these problems, the Psalms also make it clear that there is a place for lament and that God accepts our feelings of despair and despondency.

In Psalms 42 and 43 (probably once a single psalm) the writer's soul pants for God 'as the deer pants for streams of water' but he weeps day and night as he ruminates gloomily about the good old days. He repeatedly asks unanswerably, 'Why are you downcast, O my soul? Why so disturbed within me?' (Psalm 42:5, 11, 43:5). Movingly and poetically, he feels overwhelmed and seems to blame God: 'Deep calls to deep in the roar of your waterfalls; all your waves and breakers have swept over me.' His mental state causes physical symptoms: 'My bones suffer mortal agony'. Yet even in the blackest of times, faith and hope break through as he determinedly speaks to his despairing soul 'Put your hope in God, for I will yet praise him, my Saviour and my God'. The psalmist confronts his despair by reminding himself of God's goodness and praising him regardless. Psalm 46, by contrast, provides the path for dealing with acute anxiety and its themes are picked up in the well-known New Testament passages of Matthew 6:25–34, Luke 12:22–31 and Philippians 4:6–7:

> *Do not be anxious about anything, but in every situation, by prayer and petition, with thanksgiving, present your requests to God. And the peace of God, which transcends all understanding, will guard your hearts and your minds in Christ Jesus.*

Walking in the Spirit

The key to overcoming these paralysing emotional states, Peter tells us, is to lay hold of God's 'great and precious promises, so that through them you may participate in the divine nature, having escaped the corruption in the world caused by evil desires' (2 Peter 1:4). The Christian life should not be one where we stand as victims allowing ourselves to be carried away by difficult situations into anxiety and despair. Rather we are to participate actively with God in taking responsibility for our thoughts and actions. For most, the feelings will follow, but even if they do not this is still something we are called to do. Christians who struggle with depression testify that this is helpful – even if the depression remains. It will often be a real struggle for Christians suffering from clinical depression to take hold of these promises and change their thought patterns and behaviour. But God, in his grace, will help us to make the best of that struggle, however long and difficult it may be.

Actively rejoicing in God's nature, truth and victory, being in continual conversation with him, choosing to give thanks in everything for all his blessings and promises: these are God's ordained ways to healthier thoughts and emotional liberation: 'Rejoice always, pray continually, give thanks in all circumstances; for this is God's will for you in Christ Jesus' (1 Thessalonians 5:16–18). In all of this we must not forget that the Psalms are actually songs to be sung. It is striking that Jesus himself sang a hymn with his disciples on the way to the suffering of Gethsemane (Matthew 26:30). Singing God's truth, outwardly or inwardly, is a wonderful way of putting one's trials into perspective, reminding each other and oneself of the 'truth that sets us free', giving thanks to God and lifting our spirits.

> *Instead, be filled with the Spirit, speaking to one another*
> *with psalms, hymns, and songs from the Spirit. Sing and make*
> *music from your heart to the Lord, always giving thanks to God*
> *the Father for everything, in the name of our Lord Jesus Christ.*
> (Ephesians 5:18–20)

Keith Getty and Stuart Townend pick up the same theme in their beautiful contemporary song 'My Heart Is Filled with Thankfulness':

> *My heart is filled with thankfulness*
> *To him who walks beside;*
> *Who floods my weaknesses with strength*
> *And causes fears to fly;*
> *Whose ev'ry promise is enough*
> *For ev'ry step I take,*
> *Sustaining me with arms of love*
> *And crowning me with grace.*

These are wonderful realities in which we can rejoice, but we need also to remind ourselves that perfect mental health, like perfect physical health, is something that will only be realised in the new heaven and new earth. The joy of the Lord that we experience here is but a small foretaste of that which we will enjoy in eternity.

FURTHER READING

- Beer M, Pocock N (Eds). *Mad, bad or sad?* London: CMF, 2006 *bit.ly/1dxqNgk*
- Berry C. Genes and behaviour. *CMF Files* 14, 2001 *bit.ly/Zr16cm*
- Bunn A, Randall D. Health benefits of Christian faith. *CMF Files* 44, 2011 *bit.ly/1oyHFnI*
- Cook C. Demon possession and mental illness. *Nucleus* 1997; July pp. 13–17 *bit.ly/1oyIDQS*
- Davies G. *Genius, grief and grace.* Christian Focus, 2008 *bit.ly/19Tgoqc*
- Fergusson A. Do demons cause disease and death? in *Hard questions about health and healing.* London: CMF, 2005 *bit.ly/1dxcTe1*
- Harrison G. The new biblical counselling: A challenge to 'Christian' psychiatrists. *Triple Helix* 2011; Easter pp. 8–10 *bit.ly/1qhnTA1*
- Land N. Psychiatry and Christianity: Poles Apart? (1) *Nucleus* 2002; Autumn pp. 13–19 *bit.ly/1oyIEo4*
- Land N. Psychiatry and Christianity: Poles Apart? (2) *Nucleus* 2003; Summer pp. 12–20 *bit.ly/1oyIEo2*
- Saunders P. The Mind–Body Problem. *CMF Files* 18, 2002 *bit.ly/1oyIEo1*
- Sims A. Gender Identity Disorder. *CMF Files* 25, 2004 *bit.ly/Zr17wX*
- Stammers T. Treasures of the darkness. *Triple Helix* 2009; Winter pp. 14–15 *bit.ly/Zr17wW*
- Williams C et al. *I'm not supposed to feel like this.* Hodder and Stoughton, 2002 *bit.ly/18bd8V5*
- Williams C, Wiffen B. Depression and cognitive behavioural therapy. *CMF Files* 53, 2014 *bit.ly/1snLLFh*

CHAPTER 6

END OF LIFE
HOW SHOULD LIFE END?

I am nothing but skin and bones...
I know that my redeemer lives, and that in the end
he will stand on the earth.
And after my skin has been destroyed,
yet in my flesh I will see God;
I myself will see him with my own eyes – I, and not another.
How my heart yearns within me!
(Job 19:20, 25–27)

The fear of death

In Britain, death has been called the 'ultimate taboo' – it is the thing that no one talks about. This reaction to death reveals our deep insecurities. We fear death because it is something that is out of our control. As Woody Allen quipped, 'I'm not afraid of dying. I just don't want to be there when it happens'. Cultures with a belief in an afterlife have a very real fear of what might happen after death. But in cultures like our own, increasingly dominated by atheism, the fear of the dying process has become the main focus. In the face of death, people can react in several ways.

Some simply deny that death is going to happen and begin to live in a fantasy world, avoiding any discussion of the issue. Others despair, give up and become depressed; depression is very common in dying patients and often needs treatment in addition to their medical condition.

Others accept the diagnosis and outlook and seek palliative treatment that will control their symptoms and make dying as comfortable as possible. And some may try to exert control over death by asking for the euthanasia needle or an overdose of sleeping tablets.

> Joshua developed prostate cancer in his 60s which spread to his bones, producing pain in his spine that proved difficult to control. The secondary tumour deposits eventually led to compression of his spinal cord and he became paralysed from the waist down and lost control over his bladder requiring the fitting of a catheter. At times he was in agony but a palliative care referral led to improvement in pain control which did not leave him completely free of discomfort but at least made things manageable. But, despite this, Joshua became increasingly angry and bitter and said that he had lost all desire to live. He begged for the euthanasia needle. His extended family visited less and less but his daughter faithfully came daily just to sit and be with him. Many people were praying and one day she noticed a huge improvement in his demeanour. He testified that he had found again the faith of his youth and was now ready to die in peace. Over the next 48 hours he developed pneumonia which proved resistant to treatment and he quietly slipped away.

Doctors, being human, are subject to the same pressures and temptations when caring for the terminally ill. Some may deny to the patient that death is going to happen by telling subtle lies about the diagnosis or outlook or by using jargon that the patient may not understand. Thankfully, this is less common now than it was in the past. Others may simply despair of the patient and look for someone they can spend their time on more effectively. The dying patient becomes someone to avoid because he or she speaks to them of their failure to offer a cure. Sometimes doctors will just hurry past the door rather than going in and facing the fact that, despite their best efforts, the patient is going to die. Some may fight death in their patients, continuing to use therapeutic interventions of ever diminishing value when all hope of a cure has passed and symptom control will be limited (eg chemotherapy for some advanced tumours).

Euthanasia and assisted suicide

Euthanasia (being killed by a doctor) and assisted suicide (being helped to kill oneself) are both still illegal in Britain under the murder law and Suicide Act (1961) respectively. However, there is on-going pressure to change the law on the basis of high profile cases which are being taken through the courts or being highlighted in the media. Euthanasia or assisted suicide, or both, have now been legalised in a small number of European countries and US states. However, opposition to legalisation from faith groups (not just Christian), the medical profession and disabled people's advocates has been strong. These groups argue that changing the law leaves vulnerable people open to exploitation and abuse. So far this has held sway with politicians around the world and as a result very few countries have legalised euthanasia. Having said this, it is simply human to agonise deeply about rights and wrongs in really hard cases.

We need to be clear about what euthanasia is and what it isn't. When a mentally competent patient refuses life-saving medical treatment and so dies from their illness, that is not euthanasia. Equally when a doctor withholds or withdraws an intrusive or burdensome medical treatment, in circumstances where its side-effects outweigh any benefit it may bring in relieving suffering or extending life and the patient dies from his underlying illness, that is not euthanasia. Neither is it euthanasia when a doctor, intending purely to relieve severe symptoms, gives medicine which has the secondary unintended effect of shortening life. That is known as 'double effect' and is both legal and ethical. However, when a doctor *intentionally* ends a human life, that is euthanasia.

This is not a new debate: from ancient times, doctors have sought moral guidelines to guide members of the profession and to safeguard patients. They have all opposed euthanasia. The Hippocratic Oath, which dates to the fifth century BC, states, 'I will give no deadly medicine to anyone if asked nor suggest such counsel'. The Declaration of Geneva was drafted after the Second World War in 1948 in response to the war crimes performed by Nazi doctors. It says, 'I will maintain the utmost respect for human life from the time of conception'. The International Code of Medical Ethics, written one year later, says that 'a doctor must always bear in mind the obligation of preserving human life from the time of conception until death'. The World Medical Association adopted the Statement of Marbella in 1992. This states that 'assisted suicide, like euthanasia, is unethical and must be condemned by the medical profession'. They reaffirmed it as recently as 2013.

Dr Andrew Fergusson, former CMF General Secretary, once took part in a vigorous and spirited media debate on euthanasia that ended with one of the participants making the following comment:

Of course, what you think about euthanasia ultimately depends on what you believe about life after death. If there is life after death then our actions in this life may have eternal consequences, but if death is the end then euthanasia seems the most logical solution when life has ceased to have meaning.

What people think about euthanasia will to some extent depend on what they believe happens after death. If they believe that death is the end then euthanasia might seem an attractive solution if life becomes too hard. On the other hand, if they believe that death is only a gateway to life beyond, they might take an entirely different view. So to help us consider euthanasia and assisted suicide we first need to understand what the Bible teaches about death and dying.

What happens after death?

Christianity, Islam and Judaism teach that death is not the end; it is a pathway to judgment where our ultimate destination depends on choices and decisions made in this life. Hinduism, and to some extent

Buddhism, teach that death is a pathway to the cycle of death and rebirth, with our reincarnated status in the next life depending on 'karma' accumulated in this one. Polytheistic religions like those of ancient Rome and Greece teach that death is an entry point to the spirit world. In stark contrast, the prevailing view now in Western culture is that death is the end of existence. 'I believe that when I die I shall rot, and nothing of my ego will survive', declared philosopher Bertrand Russell.

The one thing that everybody must agree about these varied views is that no two of them can be equally right, because they make mutually contradictory truth claims. Either death is the end or it's not. If it's not then reincarnation and judgment leading to heaven or hell cannot be equally true. It's one or the other or something else altogether.

An impostor in God's creation

The Christian view is that death is an impostor in God's creation. When God created human beings, death was not part of the picture. Human death was a consequence of the Fall – human rebellion against God (Genesis 3).

But death is not the end, nor is there an endless cycle of reincarnation. The Bible says of the dead: 'Never again will they have a part in anything that happens under the sun' (Ecclesiastes 9:6). The writer to the Hebrews says the stark reality is that 'people are destined to die once, and after that to face judgment' (Hebrews 9:27). Only two possible destinies face us – life with God forever in the new creation, or eternal separation from him in hell. But the wonderful Christian hope is that by God's grace we can look forward to a future after death beyond our wildest imaginings, bought for us by Christ's death and resurrection on our behalf and received through repentance and faith (Romans 10:9–10). 'What no eye has seen, what no ear has heard, and what no human mind has conceived – the things God has prepared for those who love him' (1 Corinthians 2:9). We look forward to life with God forever in a new world with 'no death or mourning or crying or pain' (Revelation 21:4),

clothed with glorious new bodies like Christ's own resurrected body
(Philippians 3:21) and reunited with our fellow believers
(1 Thessalonians 4:13–18).

Facing death as a Christian

These beliefs about death have profound implications for the way we
all live and the way Christian doctors should practise medicine. We will
recognise that death and dying are inevitable. We will also recognise
that human choices have eternal consequences; they affect our destiny
in the world to come. We will be clear that Jesus did not come
primarily to empty the hospitals, he came to empty the graveyards!
A person's greatest need is not physical health but a restored relationship
with God. As Jesus so vividly said, 'What good is it for someone to gain
the whole world, yet forfeit their soul?' (Mark 8:36). In case we were
in any doubt he added, 'It is better for you to enter life crippled than
to have two feet and be thrown into hell' (Mark 9:45).

*Jenny had been a very active and physically able person who
loved sport and gained great satisfaction from such pastimes
as jumping out of aeroplanes, canoeing river rapids and climbing
craggy rock faces. So when she developed multiple sclerosis at
the age of 50 and was eventually confined to a wheelchair she
found it very difficult to adapt, lost meaning and purpose and
became deeply depressed. As her condition deteriorated she
talked increasingly about being a burden on her loved ones and
expressed the wish of travelling to Switzerland to commit assisted
suicide. She was diagnosed with depression and gained some
relief from medication but her suicidal intention remained.
Through a support group she came to meet a Christian with the
same condition who seemed to have a different attitude to life
and after coming to faith herself found a new strength to cope.
'I needed something to hold onto that my illness could not take
away', she said. 'Now in Christ and through my brothers and
sisters in the faith I have finally found it'.*

So when we agonise about human suffering we need to remind ourselves that both heaven and hell put any earthly suffering into their true perspective. As the apostle Paul said about his considerable sufferings, 'Our light and momentary troubles are achieving for us an eternal glory that far outweighs them all' (2 Corinthians 4:17). In the same way the sufferings of eternal separation from God, from which Jesus died to save us, far outweigh any suffering on earth. The fact that Jesus was prepared to endure even the suffering of the cross to save us from it gives some small indication of its severity.

> ...when the Lord Jesus is revealed from heaven in blazing fire with his powerful angels. He will punish those who do not know God and do not obey the gospel of our Lord Jesus. They will be punished with everlasting destruction and shut out from the presence of the Lord and from the glory of his might.
> (2 Thessalonians 1:7–9)

So the Bible's teaching on death and the afterlife is clear. But can this help us address the issue of euthanasia?

Cases in the Bible

When addressing contemporary ethical issues biblically, we can't simply search the Bible for words like 'euthanasia' online or in a concordance. But this does not mean that the Bible has nothing to say about them. God's word enables us to be 'thoroughly equipped for every good work' and he intends us to know and apply his timeless godly principles to all situations (2 Timothy 3:16–17). There are in fact two instances of euthanasia in the Bible.

In Judges 9, Abimelek, believing himself to be fatally wounded (with a fractured skull after being hit on the head by a millstone), asks his armour-bearer to kill him. His request is granted and the Israelite leader is thus spared the 'indignity' of being killed by a woman. The death is seen as just retribution for Abimelek's own murder of his seventy brothers, and we are not told what happened, if anything, to the armour-bearer (Judges 9:52–55).

In the second case, an Amalekite despatches the mortally injured Saul, still alive after a failed attempt at suicide. 'I happened to be on Mount Gilboa', the young man said, 'and there was Saul, leaning on his spear, with the chariots and their drivers in hot pursuit. When he turned around and saw me, he called out to me and I said, "What can I do?"…Then he said to me "Stand here by me and kill me. I'm in the throes of death but I'm still alive." So I stood beside him and killed him because I knew that after he had fallen he could not survive' (2 Samuel 1:6–10).

Whether the story is true (it varies from the account of Saul's death at the end of 1 Samuel 31 in which he successfully committed suicide) or is the Amalekite's fabrication in order to win favour in David's eyes for despatching Saul and delivering him the crown, the new king's reaction is interesting. 'Why weren't you afraid to lift your hand to destroy the Lord's anointed?' (2 Samuel 1:14), David asks, and then apparently before receiving a reply, as if the confession in itself were sufficient grounds for a judgment to be made, orders the Amalekite's execution. In the mind of David at least, the 'compassionate killing' of Saul constituted a capital offence, despite him being in great pain and close to death without the possibility of painkillers, and most significantly of all, despite Saul's own request to be killed.

These two cases demonstrate the two main arguments for euthanasia: autonomy ('death with dignity') and compassion ('release from suffering'). But we must be careful not to derive moral principles solely from narrative passages in Scripture. We need to look at the Bible's overall teaching.

Why is euthanasia wrong?

Genesis teaches us that human beings are unique; we are made in the image of God (Genesis 1:26) and it is on this basis that God declares murder punishable by death (Genesis 9:6–7). Because of this, humans are not to be unjustly killed. All human beings belong to God (Psalm 24:1) and will be held accountable to him for their actions (Revelation 20:11–15, 21:8, 22:14–15).

The sixth commandment, traditionally translated as 'You shall not kill' formalised the prohibition against killing legally innocent people (Exodus 20:13; Deuteronomy 5:17). But what does this mean? The English language has created for us a confusion that is not present in the original text. There are in fact ten Hebrew words translated 'kill' in the Authorised Version of the Bible, all with different shades of meaning, but only one of them is implicated in the sixth commandment, the word *ratsach*. Its Greek equivalent is *phoneuo* and its most accurate translation is *murder* (NIV). The meaning of the word is further defined in four main passages in the Pentateuch (Exodus 21:12–14; Leviticus 24:17–21; Numbers 35:16–31; Deuteronomy 19:4–13). These passages resolve any ambiguity for us and leave us with a precise definition of what is prohibited, namely the '*intentional killing of an innocent human being*'. Let us consider this in more detail.

Intentional killing forbidden

The sixth commandment forbids *intentional killing*. The law provided protection for accidental killing, but this applied only in very limited circumstances. 'For instance, a man may go into the forest with his neighbour to cut wood, and as he swings his axe to fell a tree, the head may fly off and hit his neighbour and kill him' (Deuteronomy 19:5). Killing resulting from negligence was not excused as unintentional (Exodus 21:29). Neither was killing 'in hostility' even if not necessarily premeditated (Numbers 35:21).

Innocent people protected

The commandment forbids the killing of an *innocent person*. Under the Old Covenant, God authorised or permitted killing in three situations: in the context of holy war, for capital offences and in proportionate self-defence (Exodus 22:2). The holy war conditions are clearly spelt out by Moses (Deuteronomy 20:10–18). There were also over 20 capital offences ranging from murder to contempt of court. In these situations the Israelites had the obligation of carrying out the judicial killing as God's representatives. The self-defence provision only operated if someone who had broken into a house after dark was killed by the owner in protection of his family and property. God only ever authorised the killing of the guilty. 'Innocent blood' could not be shed intentionally under any circumstances; it is uniformly condemned throughout Scripture. (Exodus 23:7; 2 Kings 21:16; Psalm 106:37–38; Jeremiah 19:4).

We must not become confused here with legal, psychological or social definitions of murder. The Bible does not support the conclusions of others that murder is killing with 'a feeling of ill-will' or 'illegal killing inimical to the community'. So if murder is the intentional killing of an innocent human being, then euthanasia clearly falls within this biblical definition. The Bible doesn't permit killing on grounds of age or illness, and there is no provision for so-called 'compassionate killing', even at the person's request. Similarly there is no recognition of a 'right to die', as all human life belongs to God (Psalm 24:1). Our lives are not actually our own. Suicide (and therefore assisted suicide) is equally a breach of the sixth commandment, and it is not surprising therefore that throughout the Bible, suicide is either viewed without comment, or is viewed negatively (Job 2:9–10; Matthew 27:1–10; Acts 1:16–20). Only God has the authority to take human life and human beings may only do so under God's delegated authority (eg Romans 13:4). Human beings can care for the dying but they must not kill them.

Exceptions to the rule?

Loving God means obeying him (John 14:15) and if God commands something clearly then that should be the end of any debate. However, many Christians today are not convinced that euthanasia is wrong in all circumstances. Those who believe that it can sometimes be justified usually hold one of two positions:

'God's law doesn't apply anymore'

Those who hold this position try to dispense with law altogether. They argue correctly that we are saved by God's grace through Jesus' death on the cross and not by good works (Ephesians 2:8–9), but incorrectly assume that therefore our moral behaviour doesn't matter to God. The apostle Paul addresses this misunderstanding in Romans 6:1–2:

'Shall we sin because we are not under law but under grace? By no means!' He goes on to point out that our freedom from the condemnation of the Old Testament law means that we are no longer 'slaves to sin' but have become 'slaves to God'. Instead he explains that Christians are both enabled and obliged to obey God's commands (Romans 6:15–18). We are not saved by this obedience – but obedience is an important evidence of our new life. The taking of innocent human life – 'murder' – is as wrong in the New Testament as it is in the Old (Matthew 5:21–22; Luke 18:20; Romans 13:9–10; Revelation 21:8, 22:14–15).

'God's law bows to God's love'

This view claims that in certain situations God's commands may be suspended in favour of the higher principle of 'loving your neighbour' (Matthew 22:39–40). Joseph Fletcher (1905–1991) popularised this position in his 1966 classic *Situation Ethics: The New Morality*. Fletcher argued that a Christian may intentionally kill in certain situations and yet be acting 'in love'. There are two main problems with this. First, Christ taught that obedience to the greater commandments of the law did not excuse disobedience to the lesser (Matthew 5:17–20, 23:23). In the mind of Christ these 'conflicts of duty' with the law of love simply do not occur.

Second, it begs the question of what a truly 'loving' action is. The practical reality is that right and wrong is simply left up to individual conviction or conscience – a return to the Israelites' error of each doing 'as he sees fit' (Deuteronomy 12:8). This has tremendous dangers. The Bible is quite clear that the commandment 'do not murder' is summed up in the commandment 'love your neighbour as yourself' (Romans 13:9). Love does no harm to its neighbour (Romans 13:10) and murder, even for seemingly compassionate motives, constitutes harm.

Sustaining life at all costs

These two positions are distortions of the Bible's teaching used to support euthanasia. But there is also a third danger that in striving to hold biblical morality against euthanasia we may fall into the trap of going to the opposite extreme, striving to sustain life at all costs. Attainable goals of caring, consoling and comforting are then forgotten as the doctor, driven more by guilt than compassion, feels he must do everything technologically possible for the patient. The result is that the most important principles of love, justice and mercy are ultimately lost sight of (Matthew 23:23). We need to recognise that there comes a point when death is inevitable and when the burden of treatment outweighs its benefit. It is not euthanasia to withdraw treatment in such circumstances when the intention is simply to make the dying process as comfortable as possible. There is a world of difference between deciding a treatment is not worth giving and deciding a patient is not worth treating. Stopping worthless treatments is good medicine. But judging patients as worthless is playing God.

These three positions are all distortions of Christian teaching. Doctors must never intentionally kill their patients. The best argument against these damaging and false teachings, is joyful, compassionate, costly and obedient Christian care and service.

Real Christian solutions

'To cure sometimes, to relieve often, to comfort always,' is an old medical aphorism coined by Dr Edward Trudeau (1848–1915), founder of a tuberculosis sanatorium in the nineteenth century. For most of history, it was really only 'sometimes' that physicians cured disease and just a bit more often that they relieved suffering. Much of what they did was to comfort. But today, we think of medicine primarily in terms of the interventions we can perform.

This wise saying is a reminder that the doctor's role in relieving suffering or providing comfort is as important as her role in curing disease. For someone dying in pain it may seem that we have only two equally undesirable alternatives to choose from – either 'living hell' or the euthanasia needle. But there is a third way – the way of the cross. Jesus calls us to walk in his footsteps, giving our whole selves in service of others (Matthew 22:37–40; Mark 8:34;

Philippians 2:4–11; Galatians 6:2, 10; 1 John 2:6). This means spending our time, money and energy finding compassionate solutions to human suffering. Historically, this has found practical shape in the hospice movement and good palliative care.

> Diane was diagnosed with an aggressive and advanced form of ovarian cancer in her mid-forties. As the glue who held her busy husband and teenage girls together this came as devastating news to both her family and church. She underwent a course of chemotherapy and radiotherapy which saw her frequently hospitalised, with regular infections and losing most of her hair – but with some improvement in symptoms. However, after a few years of remission she had a relapse and the cancer recurred. Further treatment produced a response but less marked than the first time and it became steadily clear that, barring a miracle, the disease would end her life. Fearing what more side effects of aggressive treatment might mean for the quality of her remaining months Diane bravely opted to forgo further aggressive treatment and enjoy what time she had left. She remained cheerful throughout and a great source of strength to her family. The end was quick but good palliative care enabled her to die relatively comfortably at home.

Palliative care acknowledges the inevitability of death and seeks to address the needs of the dying patient. Pioneered in large part by Christian doctors, this is now a recognised and growing medical specialty, meaning that care of the dying is better than ever before. Management of pain and other symptoms and provision of psychological, social and spiritual support is paramount and its goal is the achievement of the best quality of life for patients and their families.

Naomi was an elderly Christian lady who had been widowed two decades before she reached her 90th birthday and had enjoyed a long life of good health and a satisfying old age with her three children and ten grandchildren who often visited. But then she suffered a series of strokes that took her, from being nimble and independent, to being bedbound and dependent in a nursing home. The latest episode left her deeply drowsy and completely paralysed down her right side and unable to speak. When she developed a severe chest infection some of the family wanted her treated but they were eventually persuaded that death was imminent and inevitable and that the key priority was to make her as comfortable as possible. It was felt that giving her antibiotics through a drip would make her last hours worse and would add nothing to her care. She died with her family by her side.

Good palliative care has proved that the physical symptoms of terminal illness such as pain, breathlessness, nausea and vomiting can be largely controlled. It is the non-physical symptoms – the actual and the imminent losses – which are harder for medicine to treat. But this is where Christian hope is so vital. The whole church can be involved through prayer and service in bringing about that hope.

But perhaps the most powerful Christian argument against euthanasia is that death is not the end. For those who do not know God, euthanasia is not a 'merciful release' at all. It may rather be propelling them towards a judgment for which they are unprepared followed by eternal separation from God in hell (Hebrews 9:27; Revelation 20:15) Thus it may be the worst thing we could ever do for them!

Euthanasia is wrong fundamentally because God has said it is wrong – and when, as Christians, we are tempted to consider it, perhaps even seeing it as a quick track to heaven, our response needs to be quite simply 'it is written; you shall not murder' (Matthew 4:4, 7, 10). The end can never justify the means. We cannot 'do evil that good may result' (Romans 3:8). However, as well as being right, God's laws also make good sense. We can therefore argue effectively against the legalisation of euthanasia in a secular forum even when our opponents don't accept that God exists. So where does this leave us with respect to our key question on how life should end?

The Christian view means that although death is an enemy, we should not pursue or accept inappropriate, useless or harmful interventions when all hope of a cure is gone. Over-treatment can be as bad as under-treatment in the wrong hands. The famous preacher and medical doctor Martyn Lloyd-Jones (1899–1981) said during his final illness, 'Don't try to hold me back from the glory'. He did not want to prolong the dying process unnecessarily and recognised what the Bible calls 'a time to die' (Ecclesiastes 3:2).

Holding a biblical view of death will also mean we don't see euthanasia as a solution – doctors will know that the end of relieving suffering never justifies the means of killing. Rather they must do their utmost to relieve patients' symptoms, recognising that they may be suffering spiritual and emotional pain as well as physical pain. Likewise, patients who embrace the Christian faith can take comfort as they face death. Under God's sovereign hand suffering is not purposeless (Romans 8:28), and the glory of the resurrection bodies that await us in the new creation are beyond compare with the pain and suffering of the fallen world we now inhabit (Romans 8:18–25; 2 Corinthians 4:16–17).

So we should not deny the reality of death or that suffering is part of the human condition. We must all recognise that our greatest need is to face death having made peace with God. Finally, we will not despair in the face of death because we have a sure and certain hope of something far better beyond the grave.

FURTHER READING

- Drain A. *Code red: A young Christian surgeon finds Job helps him face death*. London: CMF, 2010 *bit.ly/yWDefI*
- Fergusson A. Why we shouldn't legalise euthanasia. *Nucleus* 2005; Spring pp. 13–18 *bit.ly/Zr2SdE*
- Maughan T. Euthanasia. *CMF Files* 22, 2003 *bit.ly/1oyL8mm*
- Moore P. Human suffering: Biblical perspectives. *CMF Files* 32, 2006 *bit.ly/1oyL8Te*
- Myers K. Physician assisted suicide. *CMF Files* 9, 2000 *bit.ly/Zr2Sdx*
- Paul J. Advance directives. *CMF Files* 19, 2002 *bit.ly/1oyL8Tc*
- Rigg K. Organ transplantation. *CMF Files* 36, 2008 *bit.ly/Zr2Sdy*
- Stammers T. Brain death. *CMF Files* 48, 2012 *bit.ly/1oyL8mk*
- Vere D. When to withhold or withdraw treatment. *CMF Files* 7, 1999 *bit.ly/Zr2R9u*
- Webb-Peploe M. Do Not Resuscitate dilemmas. *CMF Files* 13, 2001 *bit.ly/Zr2SdD*
- Wyatt J. Neonatal ethics. *CMF Files* 27, 2004 *bit.ly/Zr2SdA*
- Wyatt J. Chapter 9: A good death? Euthanasia and assisted suicide, and Chapter 10: A better way to die, in *Matters of life and death*. Nottingham: IVP, 2009 *bit.ly/173frat*

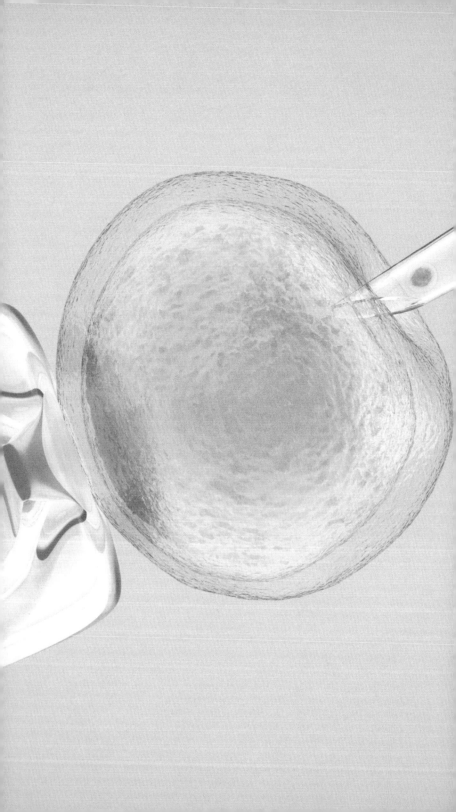

CHAPTER 7

NEW TECHNOLOGIES
ARE WE PLAYING GOD?

They said to each other, 'Come, let's make bricks and bake them thoroughly.' They used brick instead of stone, and bitumen for mortar. Then they said, 'Come, let us build ourselves a city, with a tower that reaches to the heavens, so that we may make a name for ourselves; otherwise we will be scattered over the face of the whole earth.' But the Lord came down to see the city and the tower the people were building. The Lord said, 'If as one people speaking the same language they have begun to do this, then nothing they plan to do will be impossible for them. Come, let us go down and confuse their language so they will not understand each other.' So the Lord scattered them from there over all the earth, and they stopped building the city.
(Genesis 11:3–8)

W hen Christian singer-songwriter Sara Groves attended a church seminar on how Christians should respond to new biotechnologies she felt deeply challenged about the fact that so many were failing to engage in crucial debates that were going to shape our future world. Inspired by the speaker, bioethicist Nigel Cameron, she wrote the song 'Scientists in Japan' to help wake up fellow believers to the realities:

Scientists in Japan are making a robot to take your job.
Doctors in France are growing a heart that'll save your mum.
Eyes wide open and your jaw on the floor.
You see science fiction ain't fiction no more...
Who's gonna stay and think about it? Who's gonna stay?

Who's gonna stay?
Everybody's left the room, there's no one here to talk it through

Japan is the world leader in robotic technology, but many people do not appreciate that this is driven in part by anxiety about the country's demographic crisis. Decades of falling birth-rates and increasing lifespans have led to a situation where there are not enough people of working age to provide and care for the burgeoning elderly population with their complex medical needs. In 1950 Japan's population of elderly citizens (65 years and over) accounted for just 4.9% of the total population. By 2014 this had risen to over 25%. [1] By 2050, this is expected to rise to 39.6%. This growth of older people has been matched by a shrinking of the younger population. In 1950 those under 15 made up 35.4% of the total population but this had fallen to 13% by 2014. [2] If the trend continues, it will fall to 8.6% by 2050. Japan's problems are particularly acute but virtually all Western countries now suffer from this same problem to some extent.

Some Japanese scientists have suggested that robot technology may provide an answer to the country's social problems. They could be used in hospitals, provide help for the elderly, be play-friends for children and replace humans in various activities. Japan wants robotics to be for their twenty-first century economy what automobiles were for the twentieth century. Humanoid Japanese robots can blink, smile, walk, talk, express anger and even sing.

One of the newest Japanese robots, HRP-4C, nicknamed Miim, is a female robot programmed to catwalk. It walks, talks and with the help of 30 motors, moves its legs and arms. Its facial expressions are driven by eight motors to make it smile or blink and exhibit anger or surprise. The Japanese image of a robot is that of a friendly helper rather than something to be feared or avoided. So it is certainly not inconceivable, as technology improves, that wealthy elderly Japanese without family support (or with absent or unhelpful children) might turn to robots to care for them in old age. There is already a robot which can tell a forgetful elderly person to take their pills, or not to take them twice.

1.   World population data sheet: Population ages 65 and older. Population Reference Bureau, 2014 *bit.ly/1u2hoBl*
2.   World population data sheet: Population age <15. Population Reference Bureau, 2014 *bit.ly/Zo7IYT*

A computer or robot's ability to mimic a human convincingly is typically measured using the Turing test, in which a human holds a text-based conversation with an unknown correspondent. If the human cannot tell whether they are conversing with another human or a computer, then the computer has passed the test. The indications are that Japan is not far off achieving this with some of its more sophisticated robots. But robotics is just one of many areas where technology is dramatically impacting healthcare and lifestyles.

New technologies galore

The technologies authorised under the Human Fertilisation and Embryology Act 1991 were initially aimed at providing treatments like in vitro fertilisation (IVF) and gamete intra-fallopian transfer (GIFT) for infertility. But in doing so, the Act also allowed embryo experimentation, donation of eggs and sperm and surrogacy, so that a child can now effectively have five different parents. Now we have embryo selection, pre-implantation genetic diagnosis, embryonic cloning, genetic engineering, animal–human hybrids and the production of three-parent embryos. 'Saviour siblings' involve producing genetically healthy brothers or sisters to be a source of tissue or material for a baby or child with a disease caused by a bad gene.

Kate and Rupert had a baby with achondroplasia (a severe form of dwarfism) and were advised after investigation that this was caused by a rare gene Kate carried that she could potentially pass on to other children. They were advised to undergo pre-implantation genetic diagnosis (PGD) whereby embryos carrying the gene could be identified after IVF in a laboratory and discarded rather than being implanted. The couple however, believing that life should be shown the utmost respect from the time of conception, felt that this amounted to destroying lives just because they carried a disability. However rather than taking the chance of having another affected baby they instead arranged to adopt.

Most of these so-called 'advances' have been justified on the grounds that they will prevent human suffering. Some argue that human embryos might prove to be a source of stem cells for transplant to treat people with diseases like Parkinson's disease, diabetes and damage to the spinal cord. Some scientists would like to push the boundaries much further, promoting *animal–human hybrids* as an extra cheap source of stem cells for research given the difficulties and dangers of procuring large numbers of human eggs. Adult stem cells, derived from bone marrow, umbilical cord or (now) a whole host of other tissues have been used in treatment of blood diseases like leukaemia for many years and are now being trialled for a broad range of diseases involving other body tissues.

Advances in *adult stem cell technology* have also been behind hopes that whole organs may in future be able to be grown in the laboratory on synthetic templates and lessen the need for organ donation. *Nanotechnology* opens the possibility of producing tiny molecular machines that will enable us to 'engineer' minute biochemical systems at an atomic level. *Cybernetics* involves merging human tissue with mechanical or electrical devices in order to restore lost function or enhance human abilities and is no longer the stuff of science fiction. With retinal implants, cyborgs – part human, part machine – may be just around the corner. Some scientists, among them Oxford academics Nick Bostrom and Julian Savulescu, suggest that we might be able to use nanotechnology and cybernetics together to create 'trans-humans'. In other words they would like to take control of and develop human evolution to produce a better species. Now that we have unravelled the human genome, and are growing in our understanding of what genetic malfunctions might underlie various diseases, others argue that it might be possible to engineer genes in living humans – from embryos to adults – to correct these. New drug treatments are being developed not just to treat diseases but also to 'improve' human performance to new levels for example Viagra to enhance sexual performance and modafinil to heighten concentration and memory.

What drives us?

Bioethicist Robert Song argues that the development of new technologies is driven 'not primarily by commerce, government or health-related goals but the deep cultural desires and needs that technology fulfils'. [3] He attributes the origin of this drive to the 'Baconian project' (named after scientist Sir Francis Bacon (1561–1626)), which 'considered suffering as pointless and sought to eliminate it by the instrumental control of nature'. He makes three key observations about new technologies:

Mixed consequences

Any given technology can be both good and bad. A computer can be used to word-process a ground-breaking article for a scientific journal, or to produce and access pornography or disseminate viruses or information about bomb-making. Drugs can cure or kill. We cannot be Luddites, rejecting all technology. After all, we all benefit from anaesthetics and drive cars. So the real question is how we discern between good and bad uses in order to decide what to accept and what to reject.

Discerning good and bad

It can be difficult to discern sometimes between what are good and bad uses of technology. It is not necessarily black and white. Is there a difference, for example, between using a prosthetic limb to restore the lost ability to walk and using a more developed version to enable someone to run at a speed faster than the unaided human body is capable of? Does it matter if a retinal implant is used to restore lost sight or to confer superhuman eyesight?

A Pandora's Box

There is the feeling that technological advances are essentially unstoppable. In other words, having opened the Pandora's Box of possibilities, we might end up with consequences that are impossible to control. The *Terminator* series of films depict an apocalyptic future where humans create a worldwide computer system called Skynet,

---

3.   Song R. Biotechnology and theology. *Triple Helix* 2006; Winter pp. 12–13. *bit.ly/17st898*

which ultimately seizes control of the world and creates robots designed to destroy the human race. Other films such as *Gattaca* (1997), *Coma* (1978), *Extreme Measures* (1996), *Robocop* (1987, 2014), *The Bourne Legacy* (2012) and *Limitless* (2011) have explored and dramatised the possibilities of genetic engineering, organ transplantation, stem cells, cyborgs, and mind-enhancing drugs.

Nanotechnology, cybernetics, stem cells, new genetic technologies, performance enhancing drugs: these technologies are already with us and are often the subject of government consultation, media scrutiny and new legislation. Ironically, these questions are often not asked until the technology in question is already being used. We have moved on. The old chestnuts of abortion and euthanasia, as bioethicist Nigel Cameron has observed, were about 'taking life'. New genetic technologies, nanotechnology and cybernetics are about 'remaking' or 'faking' life and we need great wisdom in using them. Technology can be wonderful and exciting and offer great benefits. But it can also be frightening and damaging. Christians must therefore be careful and clear-minded in the way that we use technology and in our attitudes to new developments.

Barry was a successful Christian businessman planning for retirement who had invested his resources wisely and provided well for his wife and children. He had recently received advice about a new biotechnology company which was apparently starting some ground-breaking research using embryonic stem cells. The promises of miracle cures were enticing and putting his money into research that would benefit others seemed to resonate with his faith. But Barry was concerned that the developmental stages of the research involved harvesting human eggs using potentially dangerous hormonal drugs and creating animal human hybrid embryos. He decided that it would be wrong to profit from such research and invested his money instead in a company developing long-lasting hip replacement implants.

Science and Christian faith

Science itself is based on a number of 'faith presumptions' that make perfect sense if one believes in God, but which cannot actually be proved scientifically. In order to do science, for example, we must believe that there is a real world of matter out there that is accessible and correlated to our senses. We must believe that our minds are giving us reliable information about this world and that language and mathematics, reason and logic can all be applied to the world of our senses. In fact, the most basic assumption of the sciences is the uniformity of nature – the expectation that the present and future will be like the past. This is a belief which cannot be proven by observation alone.

CS Lewis (1898–1963) explains the connection between Christianity and science in saying that 'men became scientific because they expected law in nature and they expected law in nature because they believed in a law giver'. [4] This explains why many of the most famous scientists in history believed in the existence of God or were Christian believers:

- *Sir Francis Bacon* (1561–1626) was a philosopher who is known for establishing the scientific method of inquiry based on experimentation and inductive reasoning. In *De Interpretatione Naturae Prooemium* (1603), he established his goals as being 'the discovery of truth, service to his country, and service to the church'. He rejected atheism as being the result of insufficient depth of philosophy.

- *Nicolaus Copernicus* (1473–1543) was a Polish astronomer who described mathematically how planets orbited the sun. From 1497 he also served as a canon in the Roman Catholic Church.

- *Johannes Kepler* (1571–1630) was a brilliant mathematician and astronomer who established the laws of planetary motion, but also a sincere and pious Lutheran, who described the scientific process as 'thinking God's thoughts after him'.

4. Lewis CS. *Miracles*. Collins, 1947 p. 110

- *Galileo Galilei* (1564–1642) is often remembered for his conflict with the Roman Catholic Church, particularly over his claim that the earth orbits the sun rather than the other way round, but he expressly said that the Bible cannot err. He saw his astronomic system as an alternate, more accurate interpretation of the biblical texts.

- *René Descartes* (1596–1650), the French mathematician, scientist and philosopher, has been called the father of modern philosophy. He had a deep religious faith along with a resolute, passionate desire to discover the truth: 'I think therefore I am'.

There is space only to mention later household names, who all greatly furthered our scientific understanding, while also holding sincere Christian faith: Robert Boyle (1627–1691), Isaac Newton (1643–1727), Michael Faraday (1791–1867), Gregor Mendel (1822–1884), Max Planck (1858–1957) and Albert Einstein (1879–1955) who famously exclaimed that 'God does not play dice with the cosmos' and that 'Science without religion is lame, religion without science is blind'.

Christianity and medicine

Given that medicine is a branch of science, we would expect Christians to be influential there also. They are. Ever since Jesus sent out his disciples to preach the kingdom of God and to heal (Luke 9:1–2, 10:9), Christian doctors motivated by Jesus' teaching and example have been profoundly influential in shaping healthcare's history. Starting with Luke the Physician who wrote Luke's Gospel and Acts, many other Christian doctors have followed in Christ's footsteps to meet the spiritual and physical needs of a suffering world. Medicine also owes a huge debt to the work that was motivated by people of faith.

Ambroise Paré (1510–1590) is regarded as the father of surgery and is famous for the saying, 'I dressed the wound, but God healed him'. Edward Jenner (1749–1823), who discovered vaccinations, Louis Pasteur (1822–1895), who introduced antiseptics and Joseph Lister

(1828–1912), who applied Pasteur's techniques to surgery are household names.

James Simpson (1811–1870) was the first to use chloroform in childbirth, but when asked about his greatest discovery, said that it was realising that he was a sinner and that Jesus was his saviour. James Paget (1814–1899), remembered for 'Paget's disease'; Thomas Barnardo (1845–1905), founder of Barnardo's Homes; Thomas Sydenham (1624–1689), 'the English Hippocrates'; the master clinician William Osler (1849–1919) and missionary doctor David Livingstone (1813–1873) are others. There is no space here to include details of the many other famous names, including: Ida Scudder (1870–1960), Herman Boerhaave (1668–1738), Thomas Hodgkin (1798–1866), Charles Bell (1774–1842) and many others. All these made an enormous impact on the development of healthcare and all were believers in Jesus Christ. There are yet more doctors and health professionals known only to their grateful patients, who have made substantial contributions in quiet corners beyond the reach of historians.

This brief survey shows that Christians have always been deeply involved in scientific discovery and medical innovation, motivated by their faith and the teaching of Scripture. So let's look further at what the Bible says about how the issue of new technologies, and see what principles we can draw from this.

Divine stewardship

In Genesis 1, God announces his intention of making man and woman in his own image, so that 'they may rule over the fish in the sea and the birds in the sky, over the livestock and all the wild animals, and all the creatures that move along the ground' (Genesis 1:26). God makes human beings stewards over creation so that they can care for the earth with his delegated authority. After creating humans, he 'blessed them and said to them, "Be fruitful and increase in number; fill the earth and subdue it"' (Genesis 1:28). This was not an invitation to strip the earth and to plunder mineral resources, plants and animals for selfish ends. This delegated authority involved caring for the earth with the same tender love that God himself would use. It was not a licence to exploit but a command to protect and develop. They were to use their skills for the benefit of human beings and also the planet.

While the Fall (Genesis 3) introduced frustration and made work toilsome, it did not remove the stewardship mandate. In the very next chapter we see the development of scientific knowledge and technology. Jabal was 'the father of those who live in tents and raise livestock' (Genesis 4:20). Jubal was 'the father of all who play stringed instruments and pipes' (Genesis 4:21). Tubal-Cain 'forged all kinds of tools out of bronze and iron' (Genesis 4:22). Nimrod was a 'mighty warrior' and built cities (Genesis 10:8–10). So we have the beginnings of agriculture, farming, animal husbandry, metallurgy and the use of the technology to develop distinctive cultures through, for example, musical instruments.

The detailed descriptions God gave for the construction of the tabernacle, and later Solomon's temple, laid plans for complex construction, needlework and metal work to provide the structures, their furnishings and contents. We are told that Bezalel, who was instructed with the task of decorating the Israelite tabernacle, was 'filled with the Spirit of God, with wisdom, with understanding, with knowledge and with all kinds of skills – to make artistic designs for work in gold, silver and bronze, to cut and set stones, to work in wood, and to engage in all kinds of crafts' (Exodus 31:3–5). Bezalel was a Spirit-filled technologist. Similarly Huram, who was commissioned by Solomon to provide all the metal work for the temple, was 'highly skilled and experienced in all kinds of bronze work' (1 Kings 7:14). Solomon's acclaimed wisdom, also a gift of God, included a sound knowledge of science gained from careful observation:

'He spoke about plant life, from the cedar of Lebanon to the hyssop that grows out of walls. He also spoke about animals and birds, reptiles and fish. From all nations people came to listen to Solomon's wisdom, sent by all the kings of the world,

who had heard of his wisdom.'
(1 Kings 4:33–34)

Technology – good and bad

This does not of course mean that all God-given technology will automatically be put to good use. Metal may be employed to make pruning hooks and ploughshares to feed a hungry world. But it can equally be fashioned into spears and swords to kill (Isaiah 2:4; Joel 3:10; Micah 4:3). Noah, on God's instruction, built an ark which was to be an instrument of salvation (Genesis 6). But just a few chapters later, men use technology to build the tower of Babel in defiance of God to 'make a name for ourselves' and to avoid being 'scattered over the face of the whole earth' (Genesis 11:3–4). In response God confuses their language and scatters them over the whole earth on the grounds that if they are allowed to continue without restraint 'nothing they plan to do will be impossible for them' (Genesis 11:6). In his illuminating book *Babel's Shadow: Genetic Technology in a Fracturing Society* (2001), science writer Pete Moore uses a metaphor of a new tower of Babel, with 'technology man' saying: 'Come let us build ourselves an industry... so that we may make a name for ourselves, build future generations to our own specifications and not be afflicted by any disease or illness'.

Tyler was a lively boy who suddenly became unwell at the age of three and was found to have a very rare form of cancer. The disease responded to chemotherapy but as a consequence Tyler's bone marrow was very seriously damaged and he required a bone marrow transplant to effect a cure. Thankfully a donor was found and Tyler's bone marrow was able to be replenished from a sample of umbilical cord blood that had been donated by another couple during the normal birth of their child. Now ten years later he remains free of disease and his parents are very grateful for the technology that was able to save him.

Moore stresses our need to be aware of pressures from those with an agenda: parents for flawless babies, professionals to deliver these to specification and health economists to reduce the number of individuals suffering from expensive, chronic disability. He argues that genetic technology has potential for good but only if we are prepared to use it in a spirit of humility and concern for our neighbour. John Wyatt writes: 'Babel symbolises the myth of technology which recognises no limits to human technical possibilities – technology that is used to seize God's rightful place as creator, and to overturn creation order.'[5] The men who built the tower of Babel were driven by a desire for technological creativity without bounds. They wanted to throw off what they perceived to be divine shackles and 'play God'. God's intervention to stop them was not only an act of judgment, but also one of mercy and grace aimed at stopping them destroying themselves. They had fallen prey to what in Greek tragedy was called 'hubris' – arrogant ambition and pride that ultimately caused the transgressor's ruin.

Babylon was famous for its temple towers called ziggurats, with foundations in the underworld and their tops, as they thought, in the heavens. This was of course self-deception. This showpiece of human endeavour, this wonder of the world, was called Babel from the Hebrew word for 'confuse' or 'jumble'. We can perhaps today understand the city and the tower as a bid for human security, self-achieved by technological advance. That is not the plan for mankind the Bible tells us about at all, and as in Greek tragedy, hubris always ends in tears.

Principles into practice

So how are we, as Christians in the twenty-first century, to approach the new biotechnologies? There is not space to deal with each technology in any detail, so let's instead try to build a framework of biblical principles which we can apply in each case.

---

5.   Wyatt J. *Matters of life and death*. Nottingham: IVP. 1998, p. 68

Engage in 'double listening'

We must pray to be like the 'Men of Issachar' (1 Chronicles 12:32) who both understood the times and knew what to do. John Stott has popularised the principle of 'double-listening'. As Christians we must approach the world with the Bible in one hand and the newspaper in the other – listening both to God's word and God's world. Sometimes Christian scientists are more comfortable with God's world than God's word, and Christian theologians vice versa – but we need to bring them together. There is a lot of hard thinking that needs to be done. As Sara Groves asks in the song with which we began this chapter, 'Who's gonna stay and think about it?'

Don't depend on secular ethics

We must realise that ethical approaches based on a secular worldview are inadequate for dealing with these dilemmas. We cannot simply rely on uncritically accepting the world's principles. Much undergraduate ethics teaching is now dominated by the so-called 'four principles' approach of Tom Beauchamp and James Childress, two ethicists from the Kennedy Institute of Bioethics at Georgetown University in Washington DC. These men established a framework for resolving ethical dilemmas by applying a checklist to any proposed course of action. The four principles of beneficence (doing good), non-maleficence (not doing bad), autonomy (respecting free will) and justice (being fair) – the so-called 'Georgetown mantra' – provide very little meaningful assistance and can in practice be used to justify just about any course of action. It's not enough to say that we should just do good, respect choice and act fairly.

How are we to define 'good', 'bad' or justice without any agreed moral framework? Professor Len Doyal of Barts and the London Hospital, for example, has argued in the *British Medical Journal* that euthanasia is justified on the basis that death is a 'benefit' for some people. What do we do when choice and justice conflict? And what is it that defines a person to whom we owe these responsibilities? Are humans with severe dementia 'persons' with rights? Are fetuses? Are embryos? These key questions need to be answered from a biblical perspective first.

Hold onto truth and unity

We must hold on to both truth and unity. When Jesus prayed for his disciples, and all of us who would ultimately believe because of their testimony, he asked for two things: that God would sanctify them in his truth, and that they would be one (John 17:17, 22). Throughout church history Christians at different times have invariably sacrificed either truth or unity for the other. It is tempting to value truth above unity and retreat into escapist ghettos of like-minded people – to build our fortresses and shut the heretics out. It is equally tempting to say that truth doesn't really matter and to tolerate a diversity of mutually exclusive views so that eventually we have sections of the church being indistinguishable from the world in their beliefs and behaviour – what Jesus called 'tolerating Jezebel' (Revelation 2:20).

Emphasising truth over unity leads to schism, splits and division; but emphasising unity over truth leads to compromise. It is far more difficult to get together with other Christians with whom perhaps we disagree strongly and talk it through together. Holding truth and unity in tension requires courage, commitment and love.

Embrace a biblical view of humanity

We need to embrace a truly biblical anthropology, a biblical view of humanity. As we saw in chapter one, Humans have great value because they are made in the image of God, and as Thomas Sydenham taught his medical students, because the Son of God chose to become a man and thereby gave humanity a unique dignity.

This reminds us again that we are God's special creations, but also fallen creatures in need of redemption. We are not just the product of matter, chance and time in a godless and purposeless universe, but the product of intelligent divine design. We are godlike beings made for the purpose of knowing, loving and serving our creator forever.

Know the limits

We need to understand that there are limits to what we can legitimately do technologically to human beings. John Wyatt, Emeritus Professor of Neonatology at University College Hospital

London, has captured these truths in his book *Matters of Life and Death*, in describing human beings as 'flawed masterpieces'. On the one hand we are masterpieces made in the image of almighty God – analogous to the creation of a great painter or sculptor. On the other hand, perhaps like a great masterpiece, we have become cracked and flawed over time – needing restoration and ultimately re-creation. In attempting to restore the original in this life we must be guided by the creator's intentions, to the extent that we understand them. This teaches us a profound truth about how far we should go in restoring the image as opposed to enhancing it – with profound implications for how we use technologies like the new genetics, cybernetics and nanotechnology. Likewise we have to be realistic in recognising that there will always be limits to our powers of restoration.

> Danielle developed diabetes in early childhood that proved very difficult to control. Injections failed to maintain her sugar levels in a safe range and the family were offered the use of an insulin pump that revolutionised her treatment and will help ensure that she does not develop early complications for her disease. Whilst they remain thankful for her treatment they also hope that someday in the future other treatments for diabetes – perhaps involving transplants of insulin producing cells – will become available that might cure her completely.

Keep an eternal perspective

We must keep an eternal perspective. The ultimate goal of some scientists is immortality and the elimination of disease – and the most extreme among them believe that perfect health and unlimited lifespans are within our grasp using some of these new tools. Of course, they have no choice but to see their ultimate hope in technology, because if you believe that man is nothing but a clever monkey and that death is the end, then there is no other hope than technology.

But as Christians, while we value the blessings of medicine, we look forward ultimately to the resurrection rather than the genetic revolution or cybernetics for our restored bodies. As we get older, and perhaps begin to suffer more as the consequences of the Fall are played out in our deteriorating bodies, we look forward to our new bodies even more. We need to be good stewards of technology and embrace and develop it as the gift of God but we should not imagine that it will provide all the answers. Much as we delight in its blessings and seek to use it in the loving service of others we must not seek to 'build heaven on earth'.

Love your neighbour

We must learn to embrace a wider love. Jesus told the parable of the Good Samaritan in response to the question 'Who is my neighbour?' (Luke 10:25–37). In telling the parable he taught the expert in the law what it was he needed to do to be a neighbour even to those with whom he felt no human bond. His neighbour was someone of another culture, another community, with whom he had no relationship, and in fact whom he despised, but nonetheless with a need he could meet.

The first century Jews were tempted to view the world under the principle of 'universal otherhood' – that is that we owe no responsibility to those outside our immediate community. By contrast Jesus taught that real love of neighbour means 'universal brotherhood' – all members of the human race are our brothers and sisters – to whom we have responsibility if we have the power to help them. And this must surely include not only enemies, but also those whose humanity we are most tempted to doubt.

The baby with special needs trapped inside a non-functioning and dying body is as valuable as the greatest athlete. The embryo in the Petri dish is as important as the scientist looking down the microscope. The person in a persistent vegetative state is as important as the member of the intensive care team. The child scraping an existence on a rubbish heap is as important as a world famous scientist. In today's global village this also brings in the dimension of the global poor. What right have we to expensive technologies when others equally made in the image of God do not have access to life's basic necessities? God is a God of justice and demands that his people act justly (Micah 6:8).

Don't let ends justify means

We must keep ends and means in balance. In God's economy the end never justifies the means – we must do God's work God's way (Romans 3:8). It can be very tempting to dispense with biblical principles such as the sanctity of life or the purity of the marriage bond in finding solutions to some of the vexing challenges in medicine and society. While recognising that there is 'a time to die' (Ecclesiastes 3:2) and that there are limits to treatment we do not have the right to take innocent human life – and especially not the most vulnerable human life there is – in pursuit of what is perceived to be some greater good.

This principle has profound implications for what we do with fetuses and embryos in particular in seeking treatments for degenerative diseases like Parkinson's, diabetes and some forms of dementia. If we ignore it we will reap the whirlwind.

Focus on the cross

In all this we must keep the cross of Christ central – being prepared to follow in the footsteps that Jesus himself walked (1 John 2:6). Carrying the cross means two things. First it calls us to stand up for the truth whatever the world may throw at us – to risk reputation, credibility and career if the situation calls for it. The apostle Paul promised Timothy that 'all who desire to live a godly life in Christ will be persecuted' (2 Timothy 3:12, ESV). This may not mean imprisonment or physical abuse but could well involve loss of reputation or opportunity. This is not easy – and the bottom line is that when we speak out on many issues we will invite both the ridicule and the wrath of all sides. But this is what we should expect – it was Jesus himself who said 'the world hates me because I testify to it that its deeds are evil' (John 7:7). We must speak out both inside and outside our Christian community (Proverbs 31:8–9).

But carrying the cross also involves being part of the solution.
It is true that Jesus called the world to repentance, but then he
also carried the burdens of that sinful world to the cross. Jesus did
not live in blissful disengagement from the world, like the Buddha,
nor was he unmoved by human suffering like the God of Islam. No,
by contrast his life was one of painful engagement and involvement.
He became part of the solution – in fact Jesus *is* the solution!
This must surely mean that we must be committed as his followers
to fulfilling our role as God's stewards, using our God-given gifts
and abilities in God's way to help provide just and compassionate
solutions for human suffering whatever it may cost. That is
what we need to work towards.

This is a high calling indeed. But God never calls us to any task
that he does not also provide us with the means of grace to fulfil.
Nor does he allow us to face any temptation without also providing
us with the means to resist (1 Corinthians 10:13).

*Now may the God of peace, who through the blood of the
eternal covenant brought back from the dead our Lord Jesus,
that great Shepherd of the sheep, equip you with everything
good for doing his will, and may he work in us what is
pleasing to him, through Jesus Christ, to whom be glory
for ever and ever. Amen.*
(Hebrews 13:20–21)

FURTHER READING

- Barratt H. Transhumanism. *CMF Files* 31, 2006 *bit.ly/1oyMCwR*
- Engel J. Saviour siblings. *CMF Files* 28, 2005 *bit.ly/Zr454H*
- Jones P. Therapeutic cloning and stem cells. *CMF Files* 12, 2000 *bit.ly/1oyMCwQ*
- Leinster S. Christians and medical research. *CMF Files* 42, 2010 *bit.ly/1oyMDRx*
- MacKellar C. Chimeras, hybrids and cybrids. *CMF Files* 34, 2007 *bit.ly/1oyMDRt*

- Moore P. Reproductive cloning. *CMF Files* 16, 2002 *bit.ly/Zr454J*
- Saunders P. Frozen embryos: The tip of a huge iceberg. *Triple Helix* 2004; Winter pp.12–13 *bit.ly/Zr454I*
- Saunders P. Infertility treatments. *Nucleus* 2003; Spring pp. 13–21 *bit.ly/Zr43K9*
- Song R. Biotechnology and theology. *Triple Helix* 2006; Winter pp. 12–13 *bit.ly/Zr43Ka*
- Taylor P. Surrogacy. *CMF Files* 47, 2012 *bit.ly/1oyMCwU*
- Taylor P. Emerging technologies: Ethical issues. *CMF Files* 49, 2012 *bit.ly/1oyMDRz*
- Taylor P. Three-parent embryos for mitochondrial disease. *CMF Files* 51, 2013 *bit.ly/1oyMDRv*
- Wyatt J. *Matters of life and death*. Nottingham: IVP, 2009. See especially Chapter 5, Brave new world: biotechnology and stem cells. *cmf.li/1rGJqDZ*
- Wyatt J. Sex selection. *CMF Files* 21, 2003 *bit.ly/1oyMCwX*

CHAPTER 8

GLOBAL HEALTH
WHO IS MY NEIGHBOUR?

*The Spirit of the Sovereign Lord is on me, because the Lord has
anointed me to proclaim good news to the poor. He has sent
me to bind up the broken-hearted, to proclaim freedom
for the captives and release from darkness for the prisoners,
to proclaim the year of the Lord's favour and the day of
vengeance of our God, to comfort all who mourn,
and provide for those who grieve in Zion.*
(Isaiah 61:1–3)

D eath and disease are universal human problems but, in the
developing world especially, many people suffer and die from
illnesses or injuries that are easily preventable or curable.

In a world where technology and the mixing of populations have
removed many physical and cultural barriers, what responsibility do
we have as Christians for those in other countries? In what sense are
those in need in other countries our neighbours? Should Christians
be concerned about global health?

According to the World Health Organisation (WHO), 56 million
people died in 2012 worldwide. [1] WHO lists the top ten killers
worldwide as follows:

---

1.   WHO. The top ten causes of death (2012). WHO, 2014 *bit.ly/1oVBRDx*

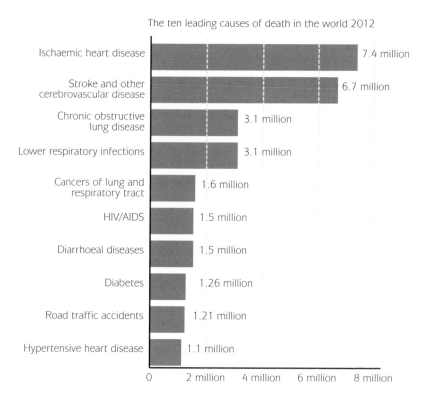

The ten leading causes of death in the world 2012

Cause	Deaths
Ischaemic heart disease	7.4 million
Stroke and other cerebrovascular disease	6.7 million
Chronic obstructive lung disease	3.1 million
Lower respiratory infections	3.1 million
Cancers of lung and respiratory tract	1.6 million
HIV/AIDS	1.5 million
Diarrhoeal diseases	1.5 million
Diabetes	1.26 million
Road traffic accidents	1.21 million
Hypertensive heart disease	1.1 million

0   2 million   4 million   6 million   8 million

Of course the distribution of various causes of deaths is different in different countries.

A world of two halves

In high-income countries more than two thirds of all people live beyond the age of 70 and predominantly die of chronic diseases: heart disease, strokes, chronic obstructive lung disease, cancers, diabetes or dementia. But in low-income countries, only one in five of all people reach the age of 70, and more than a third of all deaths are among children under 15. People predominantly die of infectious diseases: lung infections, diarrhoeal diseases, HIV/AIDS, tuberculosis, and malaria. Complications of pregnancy and childbirth together continue to be leading causes of death, claiming the lives of both infants and mothers. 6.6 million deaths in 2012 were among children under five years of age, and 99% of them were in low and middle-income countries.

Tobacco use is a major cause of many of the world's top killer diseases in both rich and poor countries – including cardiovascular disease, chronic obstructive lung disease and lung cancer. In total, tobacco use is responsible for the death of almost one in ten adults worldwide – that's 5.6 million per year. Smoking is often the hidden cause of the disease recorded as being responsible for death. But tobacco is not actually the biggest secondary cause of death. In general terms, people in high-income countries die of diseases related to wealth and those in low income countries die from those related to poverty.

Every Christian who cares about human rights should be aware of the effects of poverty on the world's most vulnerable people. Christians must be concerned for vulnerable people – whether they are children on a garbage heap in a developing world city or defenceless babies in the womb. Both are equally important to God.

Jesus the great physician

But before we even begin to think about how we respond as Christians to global health needs, we need to set the problem within the context of God's plan for the world that we considered in the Prologue. It is essential that we understand Jesus Christ's mission of salvation before we ask how health fits into it. Jesus' dynamic entry into first century Judea was marked by miraculous healing of many illnesses for which even today there are no known treatments. However, the ultimate aim of his ministry was not to empty hospitals, but to empty graveyards. Once we have rightly understood Jesus' priority we are ready to consider how global health fits into his plan.

Luke, writer of Luke and Acts and probably the first-ever Christian doctor, tells us that Jesus sent his followers out 'to preach the kingdom of God and to heal the sick' (Luke 9:2). Right from the beginning, Christ's ministry to the spirit and ministry to the body have gone hand in hand. For the last 2,000 years, Christian doctors and nurses have been inspired by the example and teaching of Jesus, leading them to the forefront of efforts to alleviate human suffering, cure disease, and advance knowledge and understanding. Many of medicine's pioneers were men and women who had deep Christian faith.

In the twenty-first century, Christian health professionals, and particularly doctors, have a passport to work in countries that those of many other professions, including pastors, do not. But what is their mandate and what should be their priorities in playing a part in fulfilling Jesus' great commission? Jesus' Nazareth manifesto in Luke 4 outlines his priorities. We are told that when standing to read in the synagogue on the Sabbath in his home town, Jesus was handed the scroll of the prophet Isaiah and 'found the place where it is written':

The Spirit of the Lord is upon me, because he has anointed me to preach good news to the poor. He has sent me to proclaim freedom for the prisoners and recovery of sight for the blind, to release the oppressed, to proclaim the year of the Lord's favour.
(Luke 4:18–19)

Stuart was a wealthy lawyer who went on an overseas trip with a team from his church to a developing country where he met a local doctor who was working alongside churches, equipping them to do basic healthcare and develop microfinance projects and women's literacy. Amazed at what God was doing for such little cost he re-evaluated his giving priorities and helped to set up a UK-based charity to raise money tax-effectively to support the work. Not only did this bring great benefit to a church ministry in another country but also helped to save Stuart from spending his money on luxury and consumer items that would not have been helpful for his own walk with God.

The Jewish listeners would have recognised this quote from Isaiah 61, which actually ends, 'And the day of vengeance of our God' (Isaiah 61:1–2). Jesus stopped mid-verse, presumably to illustrate that redemption and judgment were going to be separated in history. Judgment would be delayed in order to allow people time to repent.

The manifesto opens with the words, 'The Spirit of the Lord is upon me, because he has anointed me...'. Elsewhere Jesus says, 'As the Father has sent me, I am sending you... receive the Holy Spirit' (John 20:21–22). Jesus' mission was unique. Only he has the power to pay the price for our sins and reconcile us with God. But he calls us to preach the same gospel he preached and to love and serve others as he loved and served us. We are to follow him (John 14:12) and to walk in the way he walked (1 John 2:6).This is the pattern we see in Luke's Gospel as Jesus sends his own disciples out to preach and to heal. In these words from Isaiah, Jesus reveals his fourfold ministry: preaching, healing, deliverance and justice.

Preaching

'To preach good news to the poor' is the first goal of Jesus' manifesto. The gospel is his first priority, taking precedence over everything else. Jesus demonstrated this when people begged him to stay and do more miracles and healing. But he insisted that he had a job to do that was more important than this: 'I must preach the news of the kingdom of God to the other towns also, *because that is why I was sent*' (Luke 4:43, emphasis added). Jesus' priority was preaching the gospel and he instructed his disciples to do likewise – in Jerusalem, Judea, Samaria and to the ends of the earth (Matthew 28:19–20; Acts 1:8).

This should cause us to think: where are today's Jerusalems, Judeas and Samarias? So many people in the world still need to hear the gospel. If we were to lay a penny side by side for every Muslim in the world, the trail would stretch from London all the way east to Anchorage, the capital of Alaska! Preaching the gospel is our first priority and the task is far from finished. There are 1.6 billion Muslims, 1.1 billion atheists, 1.1 billion Hindus, 500 million in

Chinese and tribal religions, 500 million Buddhists, 100 million Sikhs, Jews and in Cults. There are also many hundreds of millions of nominal Christians who do not know Jesus as Lord and Saviour. [3]

Unreached peoples are mainly in the 10:40 window – between 10 and 40 degrees north of the equator – making up much of Africa and Asia. Many of these countries are called 'creative access countries' because missionaries must enter them using 'creative' means, such as by bringing medical or other professional help. But people from this window are also present in Western universities, cities and communities and readily accessible to us. God has brought the world to us. The cities of Europe and America in particular are the gateway to every culture in the world. Christians in Britain probably have more access to more people from more countries than anyone in human history.

Healing

Part of Jesus' manifesto was 'recovery of sight for the blind'. This reference does not come from Isaiah 61 but from Isaiah 35:5–6: 'Then will the eyes of the blind be opened and the ears of the deaf unstopped. Then will the lame leap like a deer, and the mute tongue shout for joy.'

All the dramatic phenomena described in these verses were observed in Jesus' and the apostles' ministries. There was a restoration of the whole body, both as a sign of the gospel's authenticity and also as a demonstration of God's compassion. Christians may have the privilege of being used by God to restore sight to blind eyes and movement to broken limbs, either by supernatural means or by exercising good stewardship with the gifts of medicine that God has given equally graciously. Our concern should be to show the same concern for the whole person as a sign of the authenticity of the gospel, and to demonstrate God's compassion in mediating God's love.

Jonathan trained as an orthopaedic surgeon and took a job in a large London hospital where he was able to use his skills for the benefit of many patients. But he grew increasingly concerned about the fact that many children in the developing world were suffering disability from bone infections and fractures that could have been easily prevented. So he resigned his lucrative post in England and went to an African country where there was no orthopaedic service at all. He spent several years building a hospital and training paramedics to recognise and treat bone infections and fractures and later helped develop similar work in other countries.

Christian doctors and healthcare workers are needed in every field of medicine at every level, but especially in the hard places. We should think first about the developing world. By WHO definitions 39 million people worldwide still suffer from blindness, and yet 80% of all visual impairment can be cured. [2] In 2012, there were 35 million people living with HIV. [3] The AIDS needs alone of many African countries could exhaust their entire health budgets. Yet effective prevention strategies exist; sexual faithfulness and the promotion of marriage play a key part in these. Despite the fact that tuberculosis (TB) has

2.   Visual impairment and blindness factsheet. WHO, 2014 *bit.ly/1vzaWUv*
3.   Global health observatory – AIDS. WHO, 2014 *www.who.int/gho/hiv*

been curable for relatively low cost for over 50 years, we now have the world's worst TB epidemic ever, exacerbated by AIDS and multi-drug resistant strains. The human impact of this treatable disease is equivalent to six fully laden jumbo jets falling out of the sky each day. Malaria still affects over 100 countries worldwide with one third of the world's population at risk; and now climate change is moving its frontiers northwards in Europe and the former USSR, endangering even more people.

WHO estimates that over 12,000 children aged 0–5 years die from preventable or treatable causes every day in the African Region. [4] These include infections such as diarrhoea, pneumonia and malaria, as well as neonatal problems that can be prevented by good antenatal care and safe delivery. Maternal health remains a priority, with 99% of pregnancy related deaths occurring in developing countries. [5] Jesus' respect for women as compared to prevailing attitudes in many parts of the world today is striking.

More wars are being fought today than at any time in history, so we can add the health needs of over 50 million refugees [6] and the legacy of more than 100 million items of unexploded ordnance and ammunition. [7] Alcohol and smoking related diseases, the diseases of ageing populations, drug abuse and prostitution, psychiatric disorders, surgical problems, industrial and road accidents, and pollution-induced illness all deepen the effects of debt in countries where health budgets have been slashed at a time when need and health problems are greatest.

Deliverance

'He has sent me to proclaim freedom for the prisoners' (Luke 4:18). Who are these prisoners? It is striking that just after this passage we read of Jesus' encounters with evil spirits; people were held captive by demons, captured by Satan, enslaved to do his will (Luke 4:31–37). It is a reminder that we also are locked in spiritual battle: the devil is

---

4. Child and adolescent health overview. WHO regional office for Africa, 2014 *bit.ly/1BLXsWm*
5. Maternal mortality. WHO, 2014 *bit.ly/1j1wjdy*
6. Facts and figures about refugees. UNHCR, 2014 *bit.ly/1bRcqkj*
7. Demining. UN, 2003 *bit.ly/1jZDXAT*

real and just as active today as he was then. His power base is false belief, and his most effective lie – prominent in the West – is that he doesn't exist at all. He suggests ways to lift our mood and get a buzz, numb our existential angst, gain pleasure and escape pain.

Instead of filling the aching hole in our lives with God, he suggests God-substitutes. Alcohol, drugs, tobacco and pornography create as much dependence and addiction in the developing world as they do in the West. The sort of overt deliverance we see in the life of Jesus – when demons are cast out and people miraculously delivered – is relatively rare in the West nowadays. Far more people turn from Christ today because of addiction to seemingly harmless God-substitutes than through overt devil-worship, but the effects are the same. Work, career, alcohol, food, drugs, sex, a prized possession or relationship; these can take over, distract and absorb, usurping God's place in people's lives. Many people suffer and die today because they become slaves to self-destructive lifestyles from which they need deliverance. Christians are called to be co-workers with Jesus in their deliverance.

Gwen was helping mothers in a local housing estate access welfare benefits that they were not aware they were entitled to. As she and others from her church came to a better understanding of the situation of the women they were helping, they realised that their difficulties were being worsened by drug misuse, gambling and indebtedness. So Gwen helped set up a drop in centre and provided debt counselling in conjunction with a national charity. A mother and toddler group developed into a Sunday school and several of the women attended a Bible study resulting in some joining the local church.

Many people don't really believe in the devil; others fear him. But the devil is like a dog on a leash. He can only do what God allows him to do. His judgment and ultimate destruction is assured. He had to ask

God's permission to afflict Job and sift Peter (Job 1:6–12, 2:1–6; Luke 22:31–32). We need not be afraid of him, but he is a powerful adversary. Without addressing the addictive sin and bondage to self-destructive lifestyles that so often lie behind diseases, we are not fully walking in Jesus' footsteps. We don't have to cast out demons to offer deliverance. We need simply to recognise that it is truth that sets people free and that our most powerful weapon to counter the devil is the word of God, which is God's truth. We must counter the self-destructive, flawed idea that salvation can be found in anything other than God himself.

Justice

The rest of Jesus' manifesto has to do with issues of justice: 'to release the oppressed and to proclaim the year of the Lord's favour' (Luke 4:18–19). The Bible is clear that God's people are also to speak and stand for justice. We see this throughout Scripture and particularly in the Old Testament. We are called to be a voice for the voiceless (Proverbs 31:8–9), to fight injustice (Isaiah 58:6–10), to show mercy and compassion (Zechariah 7:9–10) and to bring in the year of the Lord's favour (Isaiah 61:1–2). Many commentators believe that the year of the Lord's favour referred to in Luke 4 and Isaiah 61 is the Jubilee year in which debts were forgiven, slaves released and property returned to its original owners, as described in Leviticus 25. U2's Bono quoted this passage at a US national prayer breakfast in 2006, which President Bush attended. His main point was that addressing developing world debt, which has such profound effects on health, was not an issue of charity but an issue of justice.

Dom Hélder Camara of Recife, who lived as a bishop among the poorest of the poor during the post-1953 Brazilian dictatorship, said: 'When I served the poor they called me a saint, when I asked why they were poor, they called me a communist'. [8] Camara was extremely well educated and capable of understanding the structural reasons for the deep poverty of so many of his fellow Brazilians. He challenged the obscene wealth of the rich and the embarrassing linkage of the Church with the powerful men in his country. Like the

---

8.   en.wikipedia.org/wiki/Helder_Camara

Prophets and the Lord himself, he was a thorn in the side of the religious establishment.

Radical discipleship involves bringing justice and speaking out against the institutional evils that threaten the health and lives of vulnerable people. It involves being their advocates and empowering them to seek changes in their communities to improve the health of themselves and their children. Who are those who are marginalised today? Who has no voice?

Jesus had a special heart for the poor. Today two billion people still lack safe sanitation, one billion don't have safe water and a further billion live in severe poverty. This is an issue of justice. Every day 110,000 people in the developing world die, 20,000 of them children, largely from preventable diseases. To the materially poor we can add many other groups whose plights are at risk through injustice: Disaster victims, Asylum seekers and refugees, victims of abuse and trafficking, the unborn, those who are elderly or mentally ill.

Jesus was poor; Jesus was a refugee in Africa when his family fled from Herod; Jesus was once an unborn child. Christians have a responsibility to speak out and fight the corner of the marginalised, the disempowered and those without a voice: the poor, elderly or confused people; those with chronic or psychiatric illnesses; the terminally ill, children, born or unborn. Mordecai's words to Esther, urging her to speak out when her own people were under threat, are just as relevant to us today:

> *If you remain silent at this time, relief and deliverance…*
> *will arise from another place, but you and your father's family*
> *will perish. And who knows but that you have come to royal*
> *position for such a time as this?*
> (Esther 4:14)

Being a real neighbour

Jesus told the story of the Good Samaritan (Luke 10:25–37) to answer the question 'Who is my neighbour?' It tells of a man who was willing to cross cultural and racial barriers at considerable risk to help and advocate for someone who was in need, whom he had the power and resources to help. In giving this account, Jesus turned the question right around and asked back, 'Who was the neighbour?' When the man answered correctly he said, 'Go and do likewise'. In other words, go and be a real neighbour even to those with whom you feel you have no responsibility at all. All human beings are neighbours. In today's global village, when we have access to almost everyone in the world, that is a challenging call.

It is striking that the Good Samaritan was prepared to spend significant time and money helping someone in need whom he did not know. The apostle Paul too made a priority on his missionary journeys of raising money from wealthier churches to help those in poorer parts of the world. In pointing them to 'excel in this grace of giving' he pointed to the example of Jesus: 'For you know the grace of our Lord Jesus Christ, that though he was rich, yet for your sake he became poor, so that you through his poverty might become rich' (2 Corinthians 8:9).

Hugh worked for many years as a GP in Scotland but realised that at retirement he was still in a good state of health and had many useful skills to share with others. So he downsized his home and used some of his savings to help finance trips to train GPs in developing countries. He met up with others doing the same thing and developed a course that others could use. On his frequent trips abroad he was able to help by teaching in a new Bible college in the area and to pay for Bibles, commentaries and text books to resource it.

The global disparities of wealth in our world are huge. The richest fifth of the world's population enjoys 82.7% of the world's income, while the bottom fifth earns just 1.4%. Christian discipleship involves living simply and giving sacrificially and generously. Eighteenth century revivalist John Wesley's famous aphorism was, 'Earn all you can. Save all you can. Give all you can.' We certainly do not want to be found like the men of Sodom who were 'arrogant, overfed and unconcerned' and 'did not help the poor and needy' (Ezekiel 16:48–50). The churches in the more prosperous northern hemisphere, in particular, need to return to living the gospel of Christ. Central to that is spreading the good news of salvation, but this preaching needs to be accompanied by lives of compassion, service and a striving for justice.

The Bible indicates that the time before Christ's return will be one of great suffering. Whether the end of the world is imminent or not (we must always be ready) – and whether our obedience to Jesus successfully changes the world's course or not – we are still called to be faithful. We may not be able to meet the need in any generation, but we can still show how the need can be met. We may not be able to stop the moral decay – but we can still stand firm for godly principles. We may not see many conversions, but like the first disciples we need to be preaching the gospel, because 'the time is short' (1 Corinthians 7:29 see also 2 Peter 3:11; Colossians 4:5).

And if with Christ's help we can stand together in facing this challenge then history will testify that we faithfully followed those who have gone before us. We may be wonderfully successful by God's grace in changing the course of history. The results are in God's hands. But regardless he calls us to be faithful.

Ted Lankester, of the health charity InterHealth Worldwide,[9] has outlined the huge opportunities for Christian health professionals this century to help the needy half of the world:

> *Working from hospitals and communities, in war zones and refugee camps, for governments, missionary societies and non-governmental organisations. Working short-term, long-term, as frontline surgeons, ophthalmologists,*

---

9.   *www.interhealthworldwide.org*

*physiotherapists, paramedics, in community rehabilitation or
as travelling consultants – in repairing landmine injuries and
war wounds, in HIV counsel, care and control – in teaching in
medical schools, universities, or remote health posts – in
running clinics for child prostitutes, migrant labourers and
inner city junkies – in developing vaccines against malaria,
dengue fever or HIV... what is called for is person-to-person
responses in a world more open and accessible than ever.* [10]

But one does not have to be a health professional to make an impact
on healthcare in the developing world. It is an activity for whole
churches and whole Christian communities. All of us can pray, give
and support others. We can all play a part in Jesus' great mission on
preaching, healing and justice. In his book, *The Hole in our Gospel*,
Richard Stearns, President of World Vision US lays out the challenge:

*We are called to care for the widow, the orphan, the alien and
the stranger. We're called to lift up justice and fight economic
disparity; to speak up for the voiceless and to hold our
governments accountable; to challenge racism and bigotry;
to be generous with our money and to live lives of integrity
before a watching world.*

*The most powerful evangelism of all involves not just speaking
the good news but being the good news. Not just preaching
the gospel but demonstrating the gospel because love for our
neighbours that is only spoken is not love at all. You see love
must be demonstrated.*

*This radical gospel of love, word and deed was intended by
Jesus to launch a social and spiritual revolution on earth, one
that had the power to change the world. And we were to be
on the front lines of that revolution, we the church. That was
the plan. Jesus called that the coming of the kingdom of God
and it was meant to be good news for the entire world.* [11]

---

10. Lankester T. Global health priorities. *Triple Helix* 2000;11 pp. 18–20. *bit.ly/15Yw3qA*
11. These comments extracted from an address based on *The hole in our gospel*, delivered by Richard Stearns
at the Cape Town 2010 Lausanne Congress. Full video and partial transcript available at *bit.ly/1tldthq*

FURTHER READING

- Edwards C. MDG 5 – Saving the lives of mothers. *Triple Helix* 2010; Easter pp. 16–17 *bit.ly/1oyOENz*
- Fergusson A, Fouch S. *I could do that!* London CMF, 2009 *bit.ly/14dYvyf*
- Fouch S. MDG 6 - HIV, TB and malaria. *Triple Helix* 2009; Summer pp. 14–15 *bit.ly/1oyOENB*
- Fouch S. Globalisation and health. *CMF Files* 24, 2004 *bit.ly/Zr5po1*
- Fouch S. Maternal and newborn health in the developing world. *CMF Files* 45, 2011 bit.ly/Zr5po4
- Lankester T. Global health priorities. *Triple Helix* 2000; 11 pp. 18–20 *bit.ly/Zr5po7*
- Lankester T. Medical mission: Changing the world together. *Triple Helix* 2011; Summer pp.12–13 *bit.ly/1oyOENA*
- Lavy V. *Short-term medical work*. London: CMF, 2013 *bit.ly/145M8cO*
- Moore P. World population: Challenge or crisis. *CMF Files* 33, 2006 *bit.ly/1oyOEND*
- Roach J, Roach R. Climate change. *CMF Files* 41, 2010 *bit.ly/Zr5po2*
- Saunders P. *Jesus' Nazareth manifesto as a basis for healthcare mission*. The Lausanne Movement, 2010 *bit.ly/1pFAx8t*
- Spillman I. MDG 4 – A world of difference for child health. *Triple Helix* 2009; Christmas pp. 12–13 *bit.ly/Zr5oAs*
- Sider R. *Rich Christians in an age of hunger*. Thomas Nelson, 2005 *bit.ly/1cnIxXB*
- Stearns R. *The hole in our gospel*. Thomas Nelson, 2010 *bit.ly/18aOfsP*
- Wasson K. Resource allocation. *CMF Files* 17, 2002 *bit.ly/15bG51f*

O ur own individual human journeys, from birth to death and beyond, are played out on the stage of God's great divine drama. He plans to bring all things in heaven and on earth together under Jesus Christ (Ephesians 1:10).

God chose us in Christ before the creation of the world. He predestined us to be adopted as his children and granted us redemption and the forgiveness of our sins. And he made known to us the mystery of his will (Ephesians 1:3–9). He has not left us in darkness. The Bible unfolds his purposes and intentions.

The Old Testament looks forward to the coming of Jesus Christ who will save fallen human beings. The New Testament reveals him in all his fullness. Jesus completes and fulfils Old Testament law, prophecy and sacrifice, and through his death and resurrection on our behalf, and in our place, he secures our rescue and reconciles us with each other and with himself.

As our Lord and Saviour, Jesus, the Son of God and Son of Man, washes us clean and fills us with his Spirit to enable us to do his will.

He calls us to follow in his footsteps as he builds his kingdom and ushers in a new heaven and new earth where pain, sickness and sin have no place, where he is in all and over all, and where everything is in perfect harmony.

As we await that grand coming together of all things we walk together on our human journey. As human beings, the crown of God's creation and made in his image – representative, spiritual, moral, immortal, relational and creative – we are made for his glory and praise. As fallen flawed masterpieces, being refashioned in his likeness, we await our final destiny, the redemption of our bodies to be like that of the resurrected Christ.

Through the earliest stages of our existence we are shaped and carried in our mothers' wombs, to enter the wider world of the earth – from fertilisation, through implantation and development to the first breath of air – we follow Christ who was once like us an embryo and a fetus.

He gives us the capacity to form friendships and close bonds with one another as a pale reflection of his own existence in the fellowship of the trinity. He urges us to go forth and multiply, to reproduce and fill the earth.

He outlines the purpose, pattern and practice of marriage, to be treasured and honoured and to point to his own union with his body the church. And he solemnly warns us of the consequences of tampering with it.

He knows that we are mortal, that our days are numbered – through the ageing process and through injury, disease and death – and he teaches us to focus on eternity while being good stewards of our earthly bodies, which we are to treat as sacred temples for him to live in himself.

He reveals to us truth through his word to help us order our lives – fashioning us as body, soul and spirit in an indivisible whole and teaching us how to think and act to maximise life's bounties through its uncertainties and irregularities, while looking beyond them all to an eternal life with him that is utterly secure.

He teaches us to value our lives as the precious gifts they are, to obey his commands and to face death with courage and hope, not in fear and despair. And he provides us with knowledge, skills and enquiring minds, to think his thoughts after him, to understand the world in which we have been placed and to develop technologies in his character and purpose to tend for his created order and to serve one another.

Then he expands our vision to encompass the world, to preach his gospel, to be his instruments of healing, deliverance and justice as he establishes his kingdom and defeats his enemies – from Jerusalem, to all Judea and Samaria and to the ends of the earth. He calls us to make disciples who will love and serve him and live with him forever.

In tracing this human journey we have touched on eight great themes and begun to ask some foundational questions. Our aim has been to establish principles for understanding, thinking and acting in God's world to his glory. This has been but a brief skim across the surface, but my dream is that it might help us to plumb the depths of God's word and world more deeply as we seek to bring the Bible, health and healthcare together.

I hope that you have enjoyed the short journey through this book and that you can also make use of the accompanying videos, study guide and web resources to go further and to take others with you.

I pray that they will play a small part in helping us together as God's people to glorify Jesus Christ, the first and the last, the beginning and the end, fully God and fully man, our Saviour and Lord in whose image we were made.

To him be all the glory. Amen.

GLOSSARY

Assisted suicide: Helping someone else to kill themselves (suicide). This is illegal in UK law. In recent years more than 100 people from the UK have travelled abroad to the Dignitas clinic in Switzerland to end their lives. No one has been prosecuted for helping them get there.

Biotechnology: The use of living systems and organisms to develop or make products deemed to be useful, or 'any technological application that uses biological systems, living organisms or derivatives thereof, to make or modify products or processes for specific use' (UN Convention on Biological Diversity, Article 2).

Body Mass Index: A measure to determine if someone is a healthy weight for their height. It is calculated by dividing an adult's weight (in kilograms) by the square of their height (in metres). So BMI= kg/m2. BMI can also be calculated by multiplying a person's weight (in pounds) by 705, then dividing by height (in inches) twice. A BMI over 30 is considered obese.

Cognitive Behavioural Therapy (CBT): A talking therapy used to help people change thoughts, feelings and behaviours that are causing them problems. It doesn't remove people's problems, but better equips them to cope.

Cohabitation: Where two unmarried people (a man and woman) live together and have a sexual relationship or live as though married.

Conception: Where a man's sperm meets and fuses with woman's mature egg (fertilisation). At the moment of fertilisation, a baby's genetic make-up is complete. The fertilised egg will then travel down the Fallopian tube and attach to the wall of the uterus (implantation).

Depression: A mental illness or mood disorder which makes people feel sad and pessimistic. Symptoms include low mood, feelings of hopelessness, low self-esteem, lethargy and sleep problems.

Embryo: The developing baby from the moment an egg and sperm fuse until eight weeks gestation in the womb.

Euthanasia: Intentionally ending the life of someone (usually when they are very ill or in pain) with the aim of relieving their suffering. They may or may not wish to die. Although some people campaign for the right to euthanasia, it remains illegal in the UK and most countries.

Fertilisation: Where a sperm meets and fuses with a mature egg.

Fetus: The developing baby in the womb from eight weeks to birth.

Gamete intra Fallopian transfer (GIFT): A tool of assisted reproductive technology where eggs are removed from a woman's ovaries, and placed in one of the Fallopian tubes along with the man's sperm, to enable fertilisation to take place inside the woman's uterus. The procedure is estimated to have a 25–30% success rate.

Gradualism: The view that an embryo develops into a person slowly over time, rather than at a decisive moment. The opposing view holds that the embryo is a person from the moment of fertilisation.

High income countries: Countries with a gross national income (GNI) of $12,616 per person or more (eg Germany, France, United States of America, United Kingdom).

Infanticide: Infant homicide – the intentional killing of children under the age of twelve months. This is illegal in the UK according to the Infanticide Act 1938.

Implantation: See conception (above).

In vitro fertilisation (IVF): A process by which an egg is fertilised by sperm outside the body (in a laboratory). It involves stimulating a woman's egg production then removing the eggs from her ovaries and letting them be fertilised by male sperm. Usually a number of embryos are created, and a maximum of two are implanted while the rest are frozen or destroyed.

Low income countries: Countries with a gross national income (GNI) of $1,035 per person or less (eg Afghanistan, Uganda, Cambodia, Zimbabwe).

Obesity: The condition of being very overweight, usually defined as having a Body Mass Index (BMI) in excess of 30.

Palliative care: Specialised medical care for people with serious illnesses, with the aim of making the end of their life as comfortable as possible.

Polygamy: The practice or custom of having a marriage with two or more partners. When a man is married to more than one wife at a time, the relationship is called polygyny; and when a woman is married to more than one husband at a time, it is called polyandry.

Pre-implantation Genetic Diagnosis (PGD): Genetic profiling of embryos produced using IVF before they are implanted in the womb. This is used to identify embryos with hereditary conditions such as Down's syndrome, Huntington's disease or cystic fibrosis.

Psychiatry: The medical specialty that deals specifically with disorders of the mind.

Quickening: When a baby can be felt kicking and moving by the mother.

Reductionism: A philosophical position which seeks to hold that a complex system is nothing but the sum of its parts. With regard to humans this is often expressed in phrases such as 'humans are nothing but highly evolved primates' or 'humans are nothing but a bunch of chemicals running round in a bag'.

Stem Cells: Simple, unspecialised cells with the potential to become any other cell in the human body.

Speciesism: A term used by some animal rights activists arguing that privileging one species over another (eg assigning greater value to humans over animals) is a prejudice similar to racism or sexism. Advocates argue that membership of the human species carries no particular moral significance.

Surrogacy: An arrangement where a woman carries and gives birth to a baby for a couple who are unable to conceive or carry a child themselves.

Taxonomy: A field of science that involves the description, identification, naming and classification of living organisms.

10:40 Window: The rectangular area between 10 and 40 degrees north of the equator (encompassing Saharan and Northern Africa, and almost all of Asia). The window is home to the majority of the world's unevangelised countries.

THE HUMAN JOURNEY
THINKING BIBLICALLY ABOUT HEALTH

The Human Journey aims to help Christians to think biblically about health. This book is only one part of *The Human Journey* – it accompanies an eight-part course designed to equip Christians with a biblical framework for grappling with the key questions in the context of the local church.

The materials listed here will provide everything you need to run the course. They can be purchased at *www.humanjourney.org.uk/course-materials* where you can also find further reading on the eight key topics.

Find out more at | ▷ **WWW.HUMANJOURNEY.ORG.UK**

 /thehumanjourney

 @thehumanjourney

✉ info@humanjourney.org.uk

www.cmf.org.uk

CMF

Christian Medical Fellowship

The Christian Medical Fellowship exists to unite and equip Christian doctors to live and speak for Jesus Christ in medicine. Founded in 1949, CMF currently has a membership of over 4,500 doctors and around 1,000 medical students in the UK and Ireland. CMF is linked with over 70 similar bodies worldwide through the International Christian Medical and Dental Association (ICMDA).

Our members come from many different Christian denominations and are united by faith in Jesus Christ, belief in the Bible as God's word, and a calling to healthcare. The Human Journey draws on the wealth of medical expertise embodied in its members and seeks to use this to strengthen and equip the church.

As well as *The Human Journey*, CMF produces several other regular publications and books:

Triple Helix

An inspirational and informative magazine for Christian doctors, medical students, healthcare workers and pastors who want to keep in touch with issues in health.

Nucleus

Produced for medical students, Nucleus offers insight on discipleship, apologetics and current ethical issues.

CMF Files

Timely comment on health issues from an evidence-based professional and biblical perspective, generally aimed at a less technical audience.

CMF Books

Booklets and longer publications providing advice and analysis on healthcare issues and debates for healthcare professionals, church leaders and Christians seeking guidance on practical ethics.

These are all available to read or purchase at *www.cmf.org.uk*